The Giro Playboy

First published in 2006
by Faber and Faber Limited
3 Queen Square London WC1N 3AU

Designed by Jay Hess
Printed in England by Mackays of Chatham
plc, Chatham, Kent

A CIP record for this book
is available from the British Library

isbn 0–571–22822–4

₄ 2 4 6 8 10 9 7 5 3 1

The Giro Playboy

Michael Smith

faber and faber

The Giro Playboy

Michael Smith

1: The Seaside Town

For a while I lived in a seaside resort, in a bargain bedsit next to
the King of Portugal's old mansion retreat, in 'The Beverly Hills
of the Georgian era' . . . nowadays, it's a faded bohemia of trannies,
longhair public school bongo players, and midget Scousers gouching
in telephone boxes next to the methadone clinic . . . I would get
up at Z o'clock and wander round restlessly in flip-flops, on my
giro holiday, smiling at the beautiful scenery, feeling useless,
wondering what my role could be in this world, that boring
beautiful ocean just stretching out before me every day, as I
pondered what to do . . . doing nothing seemed like some religious
ordeal in that place . . . that town had a mystical quality about it;
I remember when the mists would roll in and the sunsets would
become completely diffused in the fog; the whole town would be
drenched in misty rose, the buildings in the distance disappeared,
and the grand old dreamy pier seemed to fade into a rosy void,
as if this were a town built on the edge of eternity, the last
outpost before the Ever After . . .

I got a job there helping this guy set up his little art gallery . . . it's gone now, but for a while it was a special place where all these quirky things could happen and all these strange people could pass through . . . and one of the strangest was this bizarre old man called Geoffrey who would come in and tell us about his wacky plans . . . he was very frail looking and dressed like a chap from a bygone, more genteel era . . . set in a refined Edwardian face were a pair of pained, fragile, sky blue eyes that seemed to be looking past you into a more magical and enchanted world . . . one day he told us he wanted us to build him one of those wands you see on pharmacy signs and ambulances, the ones with snakes wound round them like this:

because it was the totem of the God Mercury, the fastest of the seven planets, the liquid metal quicksilver, the alchemical principle of communication that bound the other elements together, the Messenger God who unites the heavens and the earth, who wrote 'AS ABOVE, SO BELOW' on an emerald tablet in Egypt that explained the cosmic laws so man could become wise and godlike . . . and so he went on, and on and on, and this was to be Geoffrey's magic wand that we would build for him . . . and I'm sure we'd have loved to, if only we'd had the wizardry or the cash . . .

For no particular reason I remember a rainy afternoon, when my sister was asleep on the couch and I was doodling with some crayons . . . she'd come down to live with me and at the time it really was just the two of us versus the big scary world . . . the stillness and cosy calm of that grey afternoon indoors, and the quiet, simple intimacy of being in the company of someone who's sleeping, and realizing you love them . . . that peaceful little face so unaware how lovely I found it or that it was even there at all . . . the memory of that quiet afternoon seems perfect now, and so long ago . . .

After a while my sister left and then the gallery shut down, and I was all alone in that strange town with nothing to fill the days, and loneliness and isolation began to make me strange too . . . days and days inside a room, broken up with occasional shopping forays and restless walks . . . one night it had got late and I was painting, but the domestic cosiness I'd felt with my sister around was gone; now it was as if that same room were locked in the heart of a mountain, or isolated in an airtight lunar module, and out the window you could perhaps see the coldness of space, and then the blue Earth twinkling in the distance, and you yearned for it and its life, but the distance was just too far, so you had to stay cocooned in the lonely room . . . this was the situation I was trying to paint myself out of, but the painting just ended up as a manifestation of it all . . . the painting was a sinister one, a dark and gothic depiction of a Victorian séance from an old photo . . . it was a deep gloomy blue colour except for some shadowy heads and the big circle of hands in the middle that were joined as a bridge to the world of the dead . . . all of a sudden I felt a spooky sensation I was doing something I shouldn't, that the very act of painting this séance was a way of meddling with unseen forces and opening myself up to them . . . a creepy sensation

washed through me in a wave and I had that horrible feeling I
was being watched . . . there was no curtain and the big bay
window was exposed to the vast blackness of the night . . . I tried
not to look out of it but it kept troubling my peripheral vision . . .
and then all of a sudden my arse nearly fell out when I caught a
glimpse of a human shaped shadow flapping a giant bat wing
near the fire escape! I was terrified; my heart was racing and I
kept telling myself over and over it was just my imagination, and
everything was fine, but then I'd catch sight of that horrible thing
again . . . and lying in bed that night absolutely shitting myself I
prayed to God, who I don't normally believe in, to save me from
Bat Wing . . . a few days later a friend was visiting and we were
up late quite spangled when he started looking worried . . . when
I asked what the matter was he reluctantly said there was a shadowy
human shape flapping its bat wing near the fire escape . . .at this
point I stopped being scared and decided enough was enough . . .
I got angry and started shouting, 'Fuck off, Bat Wing!' . . . who
did Bat Wing think it was anyway, turning up uninvited and
messing with my mind? I decided not to take anymore shit from
ghosts . . . after that night, whenever I got a bit scared I'd just
psyche myself up and mutter at Bat Wing to fuck off . . . and I
guess that's just what happens to people who live alone in bedsits
in strange towns . . .

I tried to get another job as the driver on this miniature Victorian train that ran up and down the prom, but they gave it to a guy who fit the bill better, a chubby little bald guy who looked like the fat controller off Thomas the Tank Engine . . . I didn't get the job in the cemetery where Aleister Crowley was buried either . . . even the menial jobs there had a dreamlike quality, like everything else in that town . . . it was like living in a place that was lost in a dream of itself . . . the clotted cream Regency hotels dreaming of themselves as the sun set over the sea . . . the fairy lights twinkling along the prom in the evening . . .the 24-hour gay greasy spoons and the drifters building bonfires on the beach . . . but behind all the magic was this nagging sense of pointlessness . . . it was just so blissful and dreamlike that nobody there could ever get anything done . . . nothing in that town was tangible, it just shimmered like a mirage floating along the coast, mesmerizing you into its magical limbo . . .

The moon was in Scorpio
and I was in Tesco
1 frozen pizza
1 pint of milk
1 Terry's Orange
was the mystic result

Living in that seaside resort in the summer seemed like a paradise, a dream come true at times . . . in the winter it became a cruel irony, a joke that wasn't funny . . . the population dwindles back to the locals, the flaked out hippies who are stranded there forever, the shopkeepers whose ethnic bead shops and kite stores must be slowly sliding into bankruptcy, the lazy skateboarders approaching middle age . . . in the summer, there were crusty raves in the King of Portugal's dilapidated mansion, The Drifters played four times a day on the grand old Pier, and the beach itself looked like a huge open air party, the world's biggest beer garden . . . in the winter the beach became an obstacle course lashed by rain and ocean winds that had to be braved on the way to another fruitless meander round the bead shops and kite stores . . . once winter dug its heels in I'd poke my head out the door and see the seagulls circling meaninglessly round the oppressive grey-white slate of sky, and the Georgian mansions looking uncharacteristically pokey and mean, and get the sinking feeling that this town was absolutely pointless . . . a bleak fog descended on my mind and suffocated all the good things there that winter, and a love affair with a place slowly dampened and turned into hate . . .

Doing drugs alone, falling out of step with the rhythms of the
outside world . . . getting up just in time for Neighbours, smoking
until the depressing comfort of watching Neighbours for the second
time comes round again . . . cocooned in the flat all day, scared
of leaving it, living on toast and TV . . . finally venturing out to
do some food shopping at three in the morning at 24-hour garages,
walking to them over scrubby industrial wasteland and slipways
and bingo car parks . . . stocking up on fizzy cobalt-blue pop
and synthetic salt and vinegar sticks that take the roof of your
mouth off and give you coldsores . . . going back to your flat
and another late night in front of the Open University stocked
up with a bag full of industrial snacks . . .

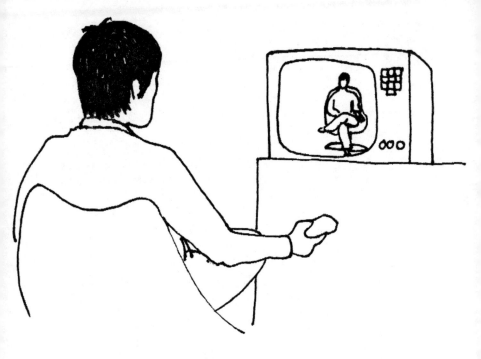

I keep the TV on when I'm not watching it . . .
when I'm listening to music I turn it down . . .
TV is my friend . . .

I was sitting around restlessly with nothing to do, so I made a list of ridiculous Canadian place names out of the atlas . . .

CANADIAN PLACES:
Medicine Hat
Emporium
Franz
Moosejaw
Moosonee
Old Crow
Padlet
Forty Mile
Telegraph Creek
Port Radium
Eagle
Ladysmith
Kootenany
Nordegg
Uranium City

And that's about the most interesting thing I did that day.

I stuck around and stagnated a while longer . . . it was quite a while longer but who could tell . . . time seems to stop when it endlessly repeats itself and you have no yardsticks or stories to mark its passing . . . I hibernated into my cosy misery, drawing a giro, ignoring the phone, one bar on the fire, EastEnders on the telly, Earl Grey and antidepressants . . . and this was how I fell into a kind of decaying half-life, too depressed to do anything about it, a tiny particle unable to achieve escape velocity, stuck in the same old orbit all winter, like the old folks going round the prom on their disability scooters, battling their way through

another windy winter . . .

My mind took it upon itself to mend my sad situation with
dreams . . . I would often dream that the seaside resort was
really a suburb of the place where I grew up and belonged to,
and going home was just a matter of a tram ride . . . in another
dream I'd be walking along the prom and I'd bump into a big
gang of people I'd known from years ago and they'd all moved
down here en masse, and we'd go for a drink in a bar on the
beach and everything would be all right again . . . and so my
problem would be resolved, simple as that, like it never could be
in real life . . . I'd wake up all happy and then realize my
crummy little life was actually the way it inescapably was and
my heart would break with sadness and longing . . .

Sitting on that empty beach with nothing to do, I'd draw little
pictures on the pebbles, little pictures about my life . . . and when
they were done I'd just leave them there, and maybe someone
would find them, and maybe they wouldn't, and they'd just sit
there on the beach undiscovered forever, like me . . . and as
miserable as I was I'd find strange consolation in certain things,
like the Giant Tomato Ride looking all derelict and abandoned
off-season, or the waves, or the sunset turning everything a
Devonshire cream . . . I remember one evening looking for the
biggest pebble on the beach, and then looking for the littlest, and
then realizing the biggest one had a hole in it that was exactly
the same size as the littlest one, and that the littlest one fit into it
snug as a nut, and finding some strange consolation and wonder
in that, in the suggestion of some secret law of harmony in the
world, and things being connected and in their place, even if it
didn't seem to be panning out that way for me . . .

Winter was slowly thawing . . . I was driving around in a car
with a friend I'd made from signing on . . . just cruising round
trying to fill up the time . . . in the road up ahead there was a
baby seagull waddling about . . . I'd taken a dislike to seagulls, I
think they'd become a symbol of the seaside town for me, I don't
know . . . as we got nearer it started flapping about and trying
to take off . . . and in that crucial moment some kind of evil came
over us and my friend grinned and put down the accelerator and
headed straight for the little bird and I egged him on in this awful
lust to run the little fucker over . . . I kind of imagined he'd make
it . . . he didn't, and I saw him go under the car and then I heard
his neck snap somewhere underneath my seat . . . we looked at
each other and squirmed and in that moment we both knew we
were bad people . . . I was absolutely disgusted with myself and
I got the sinking feeling I would be punished by the universe in due
course . . . it felt like that evil moment was somehow a decisive
one, and I'd irretrievably fucked something up, I'd just hexed
myself with seven years' worth of bad luck or something . . . that
moment felt like a turning point and a curse, and killing that
seagull was killing something else, and in my mind something
was now definitely over, gone and changed forever . . .

Spring arrived from somewhere far off, the tourists returned, the Giant Tomato Ride and the Miniature Train were up and running again and the sexy ladies returned with their skimpy clinging tops (where do they all disappear to? The Winter Wonderland?) . . . my strength was returning too, but I couldn't get excited about the prospect of another summer by the sea . . . the winter there had nearly done me in and all I wanted was to get away . . . my thoughts turned to other places, far off exotic places, romantic places, impossible places, but when it came to actually doing it, I did what everyone else does: I went to London . . . maybe 'went' is too strong a word, because it seemed to happen by default, according to some secret natural law — I was pulled in, like all things that aren't fixed and grounded, by it's absolute gravity . . . pulled in from the outer orbit of that nebulous seaside town to the grinding metallic crush at the centre . . .

It was already high summer by the time I'd got everything in order and left . . . my last night there I took an exquisitely bittersweet stroll through some of my favourite spots, past the tea gardens and the wrought iron bandstand, the impossibly elegant Regency terraces with their verandas and white facades . . . I saw two dogs whose long fluffy manes had been dreadlocked, and a man with a monocle and a waxed moustache riding a Victorian penny-farthing the height of a horse . . . the music of dozens of parties played in the background . . . the perfumes of countless flowerbeds saturated the breeze . . . the air was charged with heat and the metallic electric quality of a coming storm . . . I finally admitted to myself that it was a wonderful place, and admitted that all the energy I'd put into trying to hate it was really a lie, that I'd tried to hate it just so it would be easier for me to leave, because I knew my life was somewhere else . . . and as I realized all this a huge warm wave washed through me like the pollen in the air or the foam down on the shingles, and I wandered around at peace with it for once, and soaked it all up for the very last time . . .

2: Alone in London

A room never felt so bare as it did on that day. The furniture looked like office furniture, or something out of a hospital waiting room . . . I was new and strange in town, and all alone, and had reduced my life to what I could stuff in a holdall . . . I just sat there and stared at the big ugly thing, propped up against the bare wall . . . there were no photos, no comforting talismans, no familiarity, nothing except 400 duty-free B&H and an envelope with £250 I'd saved . . . I reckoned they'd last a similar length of time, if I found work quick and lived on crisp butties . . . in the overwhelming absence and insecurity you only experience as a fresh and lonely immigrant, the number 400 on the side of the box was the one reassuring thing; it said, 'It's OK, we'll get through this together' . . . and the funny thing is, I'm normally only a social smoker . . .

I'd landed in a pokey council flat with a frosty pair of lesbian artists I'd known from my college days . . . they were hard work and we didn't get on . . . we were in a slummy part of town that was quickly gentrifying into a trendy destination . . . I was on the wrong side of the noisy and extensive tracks, a triumph of labyrinthine Victorian engineering, thick in the middle of the ghetto, a very old ghetto that was the breeding ground of Charlie Chaplin and the Krays, holed up in a ten-storey towerblock with a shop over the road that had a sign saying CHEAP BOOZE in massive hand-painted letters with a burned-out car clapped out next to it . . . a few streets away near the Texaco was a similar shop with chicken wire on the window called DRINKER'S PARADISE . . . slumped on the brick wall outside the Texaco I would see prostitutes gouching at two in the afternoon, and one of them always had very scabby legs with bandages round them . . . there was, as yet, no sign of the streets of London being paved with gold, as I had previously been led to expect . . .

I got a temping job at an office complex that's an old converted school . . . everybody who works there still may as well be at school . . . they have to turn up on time, in uniform, making sure they behave, sitting through irrelevant exercises, being patronized by incompetent superiors, their minds drifting elsewhere . . . their lives are still as regulated and structured and out of their own control as a child's . . . everything about that office was pleasant and blank: its cleanliness, its bland minimalism, its acrylic odours, its politeness in corridors . . . there was a similar quality to the Legoland homes round the corner, a moronic toytown quality, a regression into meaningless and infantile fantasy, all bright chunky brickwork and olde-worlde style weather vanes . . . when I woke up early, vaguely depressed, I would eat some cereal and watch the Tellytubbies . . . and once I got to that office it would still seem exactly the same . . .

You could see the Docklands on my journey to work . . . I would stare out the window mesmerized by the scary bleep on the top of Canary Wharf, endlessly blinking second by second, a sinister metronome that regulates and controls London, that centres and locks things into place, a fulcrum around which the economic and social order can grind and turn in its vast, inhuman cycle . . . it reminded me of that eye in the pyramid on the dollar bill, the totem of some terrible and hidden power, a power that makes us get out of bed too early, sit through horrible tube journeys and do shit jobs . . .

belt off
his
raincoat

Getting the tube every morning did me in . . . it amazed me how
unfriendly and stony faced people could be . . . I remember sitting
near this tramp once who was caked in dirt with the belt of his
raincoat tied round his head Mad Max style . . . he had a notebook
and whenever someone looked at him he'd start scribbling
something . . . when I got off I got a look at his book and it was
full of drawings of scary hostile eyes, like some horrible paranoid
40 record of his experiences with people . . .

Coming home one evening I was looking out the train window trying to take a photo of these rude girl scrubbers on a stark inner-city platform . . . they looked so miserable and hard in that ugly station, it seemed to sum up the grimness and alienation of London life perfectly . . . but just as I went to take the picture the girls saw me and started laughing and fooling around and pulling faces, transforming an ugly, cynical picture into a warm, positive one instead . . .

Living in that dump, staying up late one night, I was looking out the window for Bat Wing when I heard two big shots go off . . . they sounded like how you imagine gun shots . . . afterwards you could hear voices and commotion . . . I had no idea what happened and felt quite alarmed, but the thing that really made me uneasy was that I would probably never know what had happened that

night, because I didn't know anyone in the area to ask . . .

43

In lonely moments like these, staying up late, prodding my favourite wounds, I remember certain things . . . I remember when we shared a bed, and that bed became a world that was separate and complete in itself . . . a world bordered by our bodies, a perfect world I could never bare to leave, so I'd miss work and forget to do things . . . I remember how that world had its own rules of time, how time collapsed in on itself and became only a present, and whole days could drift by unnoticed . . . we would lie there together not saying very much, and I'd count the freckles on her back like they were a map of the constellations, or I'd just lie there, still, watching her sleeping, and feel like my job was done, I'd reached my promised land, and it existed here, below the moon, between a duvet and a mattress . . .

I remember once, before we got together, we'd been knocking around and talking all day, and then it all went quiet, and she looked at me with those deep dark eyes, like a deer or something, and I felt I had to cradle and look after this beautiful creature . . . and I remember one of the first times I kissed her, one night in the absolute height of the summer, when you can feel the fecundity and the charge in the air, and suddenly, right on cue, the clouds broke into a dramatic storm as if we were in a real-life Mills and Boon novel . . . and then months later how excited she was seeing snow fall for the first time in this country, and how we went round the new white streets playfully trying to catch the snow on our tongues . . . and even though it all fucked up, these memories are still the perfect scenes from a life that sometimes feels like a long meandering movie . . .

When she left I couldn't get her out of my mind . . . I couldn't even wash her out of the bedsheets . . . I'd wander round my world, trying to reclaim it, but it still belonged to her . . . every street was an echo of an evening we'd spent together . . . that bench we lingered on that afternoon . . . a dark-eyed girl that looked like you . . . the night you told me you were off and I cried down the street and I found a single dirty abandoned child's shoe nestled in an old doorway . . . my whole world with its streets and scenery was reduced to a memory of itself . . .

Sifting through the sparse pile of old pictures, nice times, old faces, old friends, my girl, nearly none of them still around . . . the majority of the people I cared about in the pictures have gone . . . it's an awful moment when a person maps out the shape and extent of his failures . . . the precious clutch of people I failed to stay with, the friendships I let wither and fade, the friendships I occasionally demolished on purpose, the people and the beautiful lady who reached out to me and loved me and I let them and I used it all up and more besides and I just carried on with my own selfish pig-headed ways and thought to myself, 'Fuck 'em if they don't like it,' until I'd let it slide downhill so long it just couldn't be put right anymore and it was all crashed out and broken at the bottom . . . sitting up late in a lonely room, asking their forgiveness now they're gone and time has passed away, asking an empty wall or an expansive night sky, telling them wherever they are I'm sorry . . . I'm sorry my lovely, I'm sorry B, I'm sorry to everyone who touched my life if I was a disappointment, I'm sorry . . .

I was ambling along on a pleasant evening stroll when I saw
someone from my youth coming the other way . . . my instinct was
to put my head down in the hope he wouldn't see me . . . I think
I got away with it but it really bugged me afterwards . . . a feeling
of anxiety stayed with me and clouded my sunny evening . . . it
nagged away at me and I tried to work out why . . . maybe it was
an old anxiety from fragile teenage days when I felt a certain lack
of connection and awkwardness with the people I knew . . . maybe
it was an anxiety about puncturing that certain bubble of
anonymity you enjoy or suffer in the big city, and I was scared
of an uncomfortable kind of intimacy come back from the days
before I was happy to tell myself I was a 'keep myself to myself
kind of person' and social interaction was more complex and
unnerving . . . or maybe I was anxious because I knew once we'd
said hello and goodbye again my life was a different shape to
how it used to be and it didn't really have room for those people
anymore and I was sad those times were gone . . . whatever it was
I tried to tell myself meeting this guy would have been awkward
and we'd have exchanged numbers and then never rang each
other, and we probably wouldn't, but we were also quite friendly
once when I was younger and I regretted not saying hello . . .   49

I was on the bus home thinking about this feral little Chinese man I'd got into an argument with the other day, when he suddenly appeared and sat down in the seat in front of me, completely unaware I was behind him . . . I laughed to myself and relished this little coincidence, and the opportunity to watch him unobserved . . . after our fight I'd tried to imagine what his brutal little life must be like . . . where he might live . . . it occurred to me to follow him and find out . . . the bus stopped at the big train station and I discreetly followed him off . . . following him was a strange kind of thrill: trying to judge how far was a sporting distance, keeping my eye on him as he moved among people, observing his mannerisms and imagining his thoughts, getting excited that he might turn around and catch me through some sixth sense of being stared at . . . I followed him through the busy central hall then down the escalators, until he went through the barriers for the train that goes out to the bleakest, most irredeemable immigrant district of them all . . . and the strange little Chinaman unknowingly won
50 his anonymity back and I lost him to the vastness of the city again . . .

At night I would often wander in my lonely way and explore the area . . . I didn't mind living in a slum; after all the fluff of the seaside town it seemed raw and full on and exciting . . . it was kind of how I imagined New York . . . there were car showrooms for Yardies with names like Rude Bimmers and Rude Mercs, Third World street markets where you could buy cows' hoofs, octopi and voodoo potions, and spilling out onto the neighbouring streets, trade at its most basic level: people selling their possessions on the pavements, no stalls, no permits, just scratched old showtime vinyl and dirty one-armed dolls . . . the various immigrant communities with their terraced houses turned into ad hoc social clubs, everyone sat around on grubby office furniture playing dominoes in the street outside . . . and then, strangest of all, at the bottom of every long road, the towering corporate megaliths of the financial district, a colossus that was muscling in on my neighbourhood like an incongruous and unsettling mirage from a sci-fi future . . . and the feeling of being in an epic new dream was a blessing that made the sad side easier to bare . . .

One morning I woke up with a lovely bittersweet longing feeling, a feeling that seemed so intimate and familiar, but I just couldn't work out what it was . . . once I was out of the flat I saw the first yellow leaves on the pavement and I realized it was autumn creeping up on me like antidepressants or a slow magic spell . . . it opened up a bottle of feelings that had lay hidden at the back of the medicine cabinet of my mind . . . in summer we've forgotten completely the crisp clear light and our foggy breaths in the mornings, and by winter, long lazy evenings heavy with perfumes and pollen are all but unimaginable . . . the circle of the year is long enough and our memories are short enough that we forget the year is a circle at all . . . then one day we wake up and find the yellow and ochre leaves of autumn in a state of childlike wonder, as if almost for the very first time . . .

It definitely felt like time for things to start getting better . . . I didn't want London to turn into another miserable seaside debacle, I felt like there must be something worth digging out here, there had to be . . . and the obvious way to try and find it seemed to be to start going out drinking . . . drinking with acquaintances, people from the past, people I'd meet in bars . . . I seemed to wake up on stranger's floors a lot at that time . . . a little way away, sandwiched between the ghetto and the financial zone, was a ghost town on the cusp of super trendiness where the towerblocks gave way to canyons of semi-dilapidated tumbledown warehouses with weeds and nettles and skies for roofs, where a strange scene seemed to be taking shape and a steady stream of new bars full of exotic people was popping up . . . the place was so run down it was the closest a city gets to a wilderness, a new frontier, virgin territory for the people with enough flair and imagination to tame it . . . and that generally meant lots of party animals and weirdos, and lots of weird parties and bars, a scene I began to cautiously skirt . . .

It was exciting round there at that time because it was in the middle of a massive convulsion, and maybe it wasn't obvious just how violent that convulsion was, and you can only see it now it's complete and the interesting dynamic transitory period has gone . . . it's all a bit clean and stale round there now . . . the other day I wandered into this plush residential development for cityboys that was all steel and panelled wood, with a huge central courtyard and an enormous bronze cast of Alfred Hitchcock's head in the middle, and I suddenly realized that years ago I'd stumbled into a party on this very spot when it was still a dilapidated old film studio . . . it's a very vivid memory, that party, one of the best ones I ever went to . . . the central hall was enormous and had a huge bomb crater in the middle wall, where these sinister Detroit types were standing up there above us all in high tech military frogmen gear doing scary moves that looked like a blend of occult ritual, kung fu and Nazi salutes while they hammered out their set, drawing you into the dark and cavernous world of their music . . . their set comprised of nothing but endless modulations and permutations of Donna Summer's 'I Feel Love' . . . I danced to it for a while, went in another room for an hour or so, and when I came back it was still the same track . . . it was all they played all night . . . you couldn't help but be locked into it and they just battered it into your brain relentlessly until you lost yourself in it and it used you to feed itself as it pulsated and grew with its own dark life, like the terrible force of will you sense manifesting itself when you watch old footage of the Nuremberg Rallies . . . it was one of the deepest, most intense musical experiences I've ever had . . . and now I looked around the place it was all sanitized water features and silver birches and city women driving around in Smart cars, utterly oblivious to all the madness their shiny new apartments were built on top of . . .

The nightlife went hand in hand with this weird marginal art scene
that seemed to exist in the void between extreme urban desolation
and snazzy high-flying bohemia . . . and into the yawning vacuum
all these strange lost people were sucked . . . I remember the private
views you'd come across by chance, wandering around on bonfire
night, being drawn to some weird bonfire, and find these bizarre art
events like courtly spectacles held in dilapidated jam factories . . .
women with false eyepatches telling their overblown stories to
people who were laughing too hard, the frosty lesbians causing
an uneasy chill in the corner, flashy sportscars with stuffed parrots
stuck to the roof for the occasion pulling up outside the scrubby
wasteland . . . all this going on over the road from the boarded
up sink estates that had been recolonized by seedy squatting
communities of Polish crusty ravers and fire-eater types, where
the trendier people would venture to score ketamine and skag . . .
this was another place I walked past recently and it's all been
knocked down and turned into luxury flats with sandblasted
clean new roads . . .

A guy I was getting friendly with took me to a strange event in a factory run by all these circus performers . . . it took place in a heavy-duty industrial estate a few miles further east, a huge sprawl that runs along a dirty tributary of the Thames which is one of the most extreme industrial landscapes you can imagine . . . just miles and miles of factories and smokestacks and pylons, septic tanks lit up like eerie X-Files labs, all deserted in the dead quiet of the night . . . the dusty road we had to walk down didn't have street lights or even have a pavement, and I worried as HGV lorries thundered past us in the moonlight . . . but eventually in the heart of the horrible place we found the factory in question, and once we got inside we found a completely different world, a warm and wonderful hermetically sealed reality . . . the place was packed with quiet faces watching this amazing circus show . . . in the gentle candlelight jugglers and tightrope walkers kept the audience transfixed . . . we silently took our place by the wall . . . I looked out of the huge factory windows at a panorama of train tracks and desolate scrub and faraway Canary Wharf, and from the comfort of the cosy circus factory it felt like it was transformed into a fairytale frieze of an industrial wasteland . . . and as a train sloped by with its sad little lit-up windows my friend pointed out a candlelit reflection from the circus show juxtaposed onto the scene, a lady's legs swaying backwards and forwards slowly on a trapeze, rhythmically skimming the pyramid of Canary Warf at the bottom of each graceful arc . . . and we looked at each other and smiled, as if we'd both just got it, both just realized that life was secretly enchanted and we'd actually been living in a movie all along . . .

And then, completely out of the blue, I felt like I was falling in love again . . . I had a whirlwind fling with a beautiful Modiglianiesque woman from far away, and then she had to go back there, and a day or two later I was left on my own walking round town in a kind of magical daydream . . . I was very happy and very sad . . . I visited a gallery and half the pictures looked like her . . . songs in shoeshops were all about us . . . on the way home I sat in a drizzly market café on a street that was shuffling towards the end of the day . . . it had a really watery autumnal vibe about it . . . my fry up had a completely different feel: the bacon tasted of animal vitality and life; the fluffy golden scrambled egg was like eating a little bit of springtime sun . . . it was drizzly and grey as I was walking home, the sky was breaking in its misery, but out of the blue a childlike ice cream van melody kicked in, that zylophone sound doing 'Oranges and Lemons' . . . our estate acted as a natural amphitheatre as the van did a U-turn so the whole miserable concrete scene was saturated and washed with that magical melody . . . and that moment out there seemed a perfect mirror image of this strange interior country I was exploring, of these mysterious and familiar feelings that had come to visit . . .

When I wander round these parts, I sometimes imagine the
titanic days of Queen Victoria's reign, and the epic, sprawling
stream of life flowing everywhere, flowing like the River Fleet
beneath the Holborn Viaduct — beggars with no legs, top-hatted
occultists, balloonists crashing their balloons completely battered
on opium, barefoot Irishmen in rags, thieving chimney sweeps,
Indian holymen, floating Qabbalistic Rabbis, shifty looking
Chinamen with long nails, syphilitic sailors, gin palaces, music
hall drag queens, bearded ladies, animal markets full of monkeys
and parakeets, horse shit everywhere, smog, smog, smog, and
not a car or a Starbucks in sight . . .

The drinking sessions were getting druggier and more frequent . . . it was Saturday and I'd been up till half eight in the morning on a bit of a bender and when I awoke it was already getting dark again . . . I went to the toilet and the world fell out of my arse . . . I was all over the shop but I knew I had to get it together to make a journey into the scary slums . . . I left the house all jittery and paranoid . . . I could have really done without the outside world intruding into my mind and the darkness closing in all around me . . . the neighbourhood took on the air of the classic innercity urban wasteland . . . it was all just too close, and I felt like I might crumble at any minute . . . then in an awful moment my heart jumped into my mouth and I froze in crazy disbelief as I watched a four foot creature with a demonic green skullface hobble towards me with an outstretched hand . . . he asked me for change . . . then I realized that in my messed up state I'd forgotten what day it was: Jesus H Christ it was all OK it was only fucking Halloween . . . I didn't give the kid any money . . . the air of spooky menace stuck . . . Halloween was definitely freaking me out . . . the comedown didn't help . . . neither did the fact I was walking down the main drag of a nasty shithole in the dark . . . the street was suddenly full of nine year old witches with pointy hats and warts . . . teenage purse snatchers in hockey masks like that nutter in the Friday The Thirteenth films hung out round Drinker's Paradise looking properly scary . . . Halloween in the ghetto is not a pretty sight . . . the downtrodden fifty-year-old chainsmokers shuffling along looking like zombies anyway . . . the place looked like the village of the damned . . . and in my sorry state it felt like maybe tonight the veil between us and all the lost souls had grown thinner and a little more frayed . . .

I only came across the House of Detention once, on a strange and foggy late night wander through the winding gothic rookeries of Clerkenwell . . . I remember an alley and a dark stony exterior and an enormous gargoyled head above the door, like the door of The Haunted House in a child's dreamlike fairground memories . . . it amazed me that such a fantastical place could exist in a world as sober as this one, and I searched for it again afterwards to make sure it was real, but to no avail . . . I've looked for that building again and again, in the cold light of day and the quiet of the night, but I've never found it, and I wonder whether it may have been a phantasmagoria, a dream place that exists in the recesses of Clerkenwell's memories of itself, that only appears on those moody moonlit nights when Clerkenwell recalls its ghost memories, a Flying Dutchman landlocked in the heart of the

silent dreaming city . . .

With all that happening at night, going to the temping job in the morning just didn't make any sense . . . I could see right through it . . . I was stuck on the lowest levels of a corporate reality that was obviously utterly meaningless and phoney . . . never more meaningless and phoney than when we received a barrage of corporate Christmas cards . . . the fuckers have even hijacked that most personal of activities and send each other cards completely insincerely, feigning the personal touch with people they don't even know . . . they don't even get each other's names right . . . cards for the boss, Gerry, that read 'Dear Joey . . .'

I'd had a good run that autumn, found lots of new things, but it was coming up to Christmas and I suppose I just needed to go home, needed to feel a bit of familiarity and warmth . . . one night I was laid on someone or other's floor far too drunk, falling asleep cuddling a teddy . . . that's what its all about, isn't it, as much as anything else, after all the complicated issues, we're just looking for that feeling, for the comforting warmth of a cuddle, even if its from some crappy little teddybear . . .

3: The Old Country

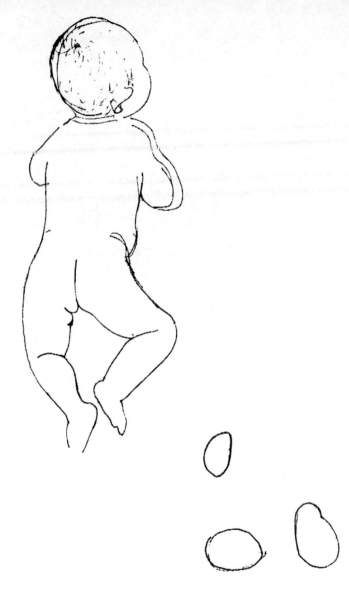

70

For Christmas I went back to the Old Country, where women on crutches wait in bus queues that last a long time, where time goes slow and everything happens a long way away, where cable TV is the cultural reference point . . . so anyway, there I was, all superior, looking down my nose at it, with this farty, romantic self-image of someone who's outgrown it all, drifting and longing for some mysterious who knows what . . . but for now I was back with my boyhood friend who never left, and we were round his house with his brand new baby: the house was warm and all the decorations were sparkling and three generations of his family were there with big smiles and his mam was holding the baby all radiant with love and me and him were having a beer and it was enough to make everything feel all right, everything for once was how it should be . . . the snow was falling outside the window but inside it was homely and cosy in the way only those homes with cable can be, and the baby was safe in the middle of it all, and suddenly it hit me, the beautiful feeling that this was the end of the journey, the answer was as simple as this — you don't have to roam the earth to find that thing that solves the riddle, that fills the hole . . . the answer was as simple as this little baby . . . God bless this little Christmas baby . . .

Relaxing in the old house again after all this time . . . it takes me back to my childhood days, living among its silences and shadows . . . in an old house like this you can feel all the time that has passed in it accumulating and settling in those shadows, enriching the silence and cosy sadness . . . the silence and sadness of lives and their limitations saturates the old wood-panelled drawing room, where I would pass the time colouring in The Rainy Day Book, or watch Taggart with my mam the same time every week, and be put to bed every night as soon as the news finished . . . the weight of this house's memories are more real to me than its physical presence these days . . . the house is being sold soon, and then, I suppose, it will pass over completely into the world of memories . . .

I'd love to find my old journals, all about growing up, the mysteries of summers, the mysteries of girls, growing pains, nicking off PE, smoking fags down the beck, disappearing deep into unknown farmers' fields for the day, dropping acid and wandering round shopping centres, general dreamlike situations . . . my memory's shot to shit these days, but those old journals are still kicking about in a crate somewhere . . .

I went for a stroll down memory lane, my old walk home from school . . . I came to a lay-by and I remembered an ice cream van, like the one remaining motif from an old recurring dream that was now hazy and almost forgotten . . . the ice cream van would greet us from lessons every lunchtime . . . this seemed pretty cool to a kid just come up to the big school, in those golden days before thoughts turned to other things, like girls and smoking fags round the back of the music block . . . the ice cream van was manned by Antonio, a fat Italian with gold chains and shades who looked like a New Jersey mobster . . . Antonio had about four fingers missing and you'd notice the stumps every time he handed you a 99 . . . some reckoned it was the Mr Softee machine that did it, others said vaguely it was The War, but no one really knew . . . mostly we got on OK, like he was one of us, but sometimes we'd taunt him with our little ditty, 'Antonio, Antonio, where did your fucking fingers go?' in a spoof opera tune style like the one off the Cornetto ads and he'd lose his rag and get out of the van and chase us . . .

we all liked Antonio though . . . sometimes we'd find him pulled up in the lay-by stuffing his face with Feasts and Mivvis after school on our long lazy walks home, those perfect walks of spitting competitions and someone always dragging someone else along in a headlock . . . we'd always have a crack on with him or maybe tease him a little for being a fat greedy bastard stuffing his face in the lay-by . . . and he was a fat greedy bastard looking back on it, but then I suppose a man who drives an ice cream van is gonna like ice cream . . . this went on as normal for a long long time and then one evening the ice cream van turned up in the same lay-by crashed and burned out after a joyriding spree or insurance fraud or who knows what . . . no one seemed to do anything about it though and we'd still walk past its burned out ghost every day, and it became some kind of milestone on our psychic landscape, a milestone in the summer that was the crossroads between boyhood and what lay ahead . . .

Lisa Carter was the most beautiful girl in the school and everybody knew it. She had lovely bronze skin and silky black hair that danced on the nape of her neck and a sultry dark eyed face that seemed to glow with some kind of sun-dappled halo . . . she also had a cracking pair of tits that were a real novelty bonus to a kid of that age, and like many other skinny and tender boys I was struck down by the aches and pangs of love that long hot summer and like the rest of them I was too tender and scared to do anything about it . . . I pined away those lazy summer evenings hanging around with my mates as usual, walking along walls, garden creeping, playing footy in the long golden shadows, but inside I knew something important had changed and soon it would all be different . . . I watched on, trying to pluck up the courage to do something, wasting the summer away wondering what she'd say if I asked her out, while she dated a string of those no-marks who are a few years older and have learned to drive and everything, those crappo Sport Billy types who somehow always manage to steal the young lookers away . . . it made no sense to me that this should happen, and I suppose I was just naïve to that fundamental fact it takes years and years of confusion and trouble to learn — that women's brains are wired up wrong and will always follow a maddening logic that drives you to distraction and busts your balls . . . but back then she seemed like a mysterious and poetic creature I saw some kind of soulmate in and consequently she responded to this and we made a connection and became friends . . . before long I'd be spending wonderful agonizing evenings round her house and she'd talk and open up and confide in whatever it was that kids that age go on about . . . I always remember her story about her grandmother still dreaming in Danish . . . the other great thing about Lisa Carter was this air of chi-chi exoticness she had — her parents were foreign and classy and they lived in a big old house which gave her something which stood out a mile in our pikey old comprehensive . . . the granny dreaming in Danish

became an impossibly romantic figure who I imagined as a young

woman all doomed and sophisticated like the heroine of one of
those black and white Ingmar Bergman films they showed late
on BBC 2 I was starting to think I should know about . . . it
made my evenings of footy and Chinese burns seem juvenile and
redundant . . . it's not often I think about those faraway times but
when I strolled down my old walk to school it all came flooding
back to me, and I fell in love with that sultry dark-eyed face and
the idea of a granny still dreaming in Danish and those long late
summer evenings at the end of boyhood all over again . . . how's
your granny doing these days, Lisa? Where are you now?

Being a teenager hit me hard, and being back in the Old Country reminded me of it . . . looking out across the sad beautiful landscape rolling out to nowhere, I remembered being a lonely lad riding over the hills on my bike, getting stoned, searching for something, something that could never be there . . . I wasted whole summers like that, beautiful summers spoiled by the nagging feeling I should be doing something else, somewhere better . . . summers staying in reading Ulysses, the nagging suspicion I should be off my nut at a rave somewhere never far away . . . but none of that really happened round here in the arse end of nowhere, that sort of thing all happened somewhere far away . . . all we got were Cure records at the indie night in Club Gemini on Thursdays — that or a wine bar full of welders and scrubbers, 'Hey Macarena' with all the meat heads down the meat market on the weekend . . .

I didn't like that time in my life at all . . . my head went somewhere
strange and went there on its own . . . for a year or so I didn't
really do people at all . . . they made me chronically nervous and
uncomfortable . . . so I retreated into some kind of morbid
narcissistic fascination with my own fuckups . . . my days were
filled with strange lonely explorations on the bike, strange lonely
explorations into the effects of weed, explorations into the cradle
of my own misery and confusion . . . I was a chronic example of
the confused teenager, thinking, like all teenagers do, I was
completely unique and the only one it had ever happened to . . .

There was a period one summer after my GCSEs when me and this other kid would get some drugs, take the train up to Newcastle and deliberately kip rough; I remember the excitement of those summer evenings, the expansive feeling of promise and possibility, of life and the city opening out for you; we'd walk round town, through all the Friday night drunks spilling out of the town centre, wander into the ropey areas round the back of the station, the broody dilapidated bits by the river, get stoned in this hilly outcrop near the big old industrial iron bridges, winding up in this all-night greasy spoon next to a shop with blacked out windows called SVEN ADULT BOOKS; we'd see in the early hours observing the drunks and weirdos and I'd write awful pretentious poetry about it in my notepad . . . I didn't really know what I was playing at, but then I suppose that's the whole point of being a teenager . . .

That phase culminated when me and a goth lass friend of mine kipped rough 200 miles away in Edinburgh . . . we were on acid and ended up completely twisted in the pitch black ancient cemetery in the centre of the city . . . we got lost in it and couldn't figure out how to leave; I kept seeing strange headed figures coming out the bushes; I was convinced we'd end up being sacrificed in the black heart of the place by Satanists . . . we did escape of course, though it seemed like a miracle at the time . . . we spent the rest of the night creeping through the deserted guts of the city, trying to keep it together, avoiding the tramps and freaks, convinced they were all after us, ending up in some seedy late night bar somewhere behind the Royal Mile, finally going back to the station when it opened with the morning light . . . I remember lying on a bench in the station frazzled and exhausted, hallucinating an enormous bright red can of coke on the platform, completely paranoid the police would arrest us for looking like tramps or druggy weirdos . . . I lay there just dying to get back into my own bed again, wondering why the fuck I'd taken loads of acid and kipped rough in Edinburgh in the first place . . . luckily that phase didn't last much longer — I started feeling all right again, socialized like normal people do, lost my virginity like everybody else; all the oddness gradually faded into the recesses of my personality but occasionally those feelings come back and I feel like a scared teenager lost in a strange city cemetery again . . .

Though all those ghosts are largely laid to rest, my relationship
with the Old Country is still a troubled one . . . it's a weird place
and its most famous story illustrates why . . . once upon a time,
a ship was wrecked on the coast, and amid the wreckage was the
lone survivor of the catastrophe, a monkey the captain must
have kept as a pet, dressed up in a little drummer boy's suit . . .
England was at war with France at the time, and the good
townsfolk decided the hairy, gibbering little fellow in the suit
must be a French spy . . . the monkey was duly put on trial and
hanged in the town square . . . or so the story goes . . . in the recent
elections a man dressed up as a giant monkey was voted in as
mayor . . . he was previously famous as a football mascot who
got into trouble for fighting giant dolphins and lions at matches . . .
his only major policy was free bananas for everyone . . . amazingly
he beat a high ranking government official . . . when I found out,
far away in the seaside resort, I was genuinely flabbergasted . . .
it was hilarious and brilliant and embarrassing . . . the thought of
it still makes me very proud and very ashamed of my town . . .
82   as I said, my relationship with it is a troubled one . . .

The stories that get back to me are always like that, monkey
stories that celebrate stupidity and absurdity, or squalid gossip
that celebrates degradation, that celebrates the fact the place is
falling apart . . . my friend was telling me about this junky from
up The Manor who's been evicted from his council flat because
he sold literally everything in it . . . from the TV and cooker down
to the beds and carpets, the lot . . . where the kitchen sink used to
be there was just a hose . . . he was getting round to the bare
floorboards when they turfed him out . . . these days you can
find him hanging round the park staggering around in his floppy
shoes and **Cellnet*** jog suit . . .

Crack and brown were really the reserve of the bad lads, or
Chores as we called them . . . the people I knocked around with
were generally more placid and settled for a lifestyle based round
smoking weed . . . a friend of mine used to own a sweet shop in
this rough estate a few doors down from Sucker, who famously
sold the second best skunk in the town . . . Sucker was on the
corner in a pebbledashed semi that had grilles on the window and
a CCTV above the door . . . he'd come to the door with a baseball
bat, but he always looked like he was about to fall over . . . a lot
of people used to end up hanging around Boothy's sweet shop
getting stoned and whatever, and poor old Boothy was always
really stoned, so when we got the rush of schoolkids going home
we'd help out serving them . . . a steady stream of malnourished
scruffy kids would come in and get five Wham Bars and five
bags of Spaceraiders for their tea . . . they'd throw a handful of
two pences on the counter because they seemed to have trouble
counting . . . and after an afternoon smoking the second best
skunk in the town, so did we . . .

All those lives that promised as much as anybody's, stifled by the Old Country . . . I remember the last time I saw some of my old friends, and we ended up going to the bingo . . . I couldn't believe them killing an afternoon round very old or very fat ladies, all chainsmoking and drained by life . . . they even ended up taking speed to make an occasion of it, so the bingo would be more of a buzz and they'd be more alert, quicker and more likely to win . . .

When I saw everyone again it was at a big piss-up . . . I went
round with a bottle of Teachers Whisky, which no one would
help me drink . . . a few hours later I was slumped in a chair with
an empty bottle of whisky, calling people cunts then cuddling them,
then I passed out . . . I woke up on the floor in the blinding winter
sun, with a hangover that was absolutely unbearable . . . I couldn't
move, but I wanted to get away from a smell that was so bad it
took my mind off the hangover . . . as I lay there too weak to
move I wondered what that smell could be . . . when I finally
gathered the strength to drag myself from the floor I realized my
pounding dehydrated head had been laid next to a radiator that
was on full blast . . . the smell seemed to be coming from behind
it . . . I had a look and caught the full blast of a garlic kebab
that had obviously been shoved down the back for ages . . . my
stomach turned and my legs almost buckled and I decided I had
to leave the house . . . outside the crisp morning air eased my
broken head a little and I was thankful I didn't have to talk to
anyone . . . then I bumped into my best friend's mam . . . as I
tried to talk to her and fight off the nausea I noticed a huge streak
of fatty, pink, raw bacon glistening on the dirty, frosty pavement
in front of me . . . my stomach nearly turned again and I had to
make my excuses and go . . . I've never touched Teachers Whisky
again and the ghosts of a rotten garlic kebab and a giant streak
of raw bacon still haunt my queasier hangovers . . .

I bumped into Wormy one afternoon when I was 'down the town' and ended up round his new flat . . . he was living off Murray St, the decaying Victorian giroland between the town centre and the Barratt suburbs . . . I'd just been given a sheet of mazzies by a girl who stole them off her manically depressed father . . . they were these very strong ones shaped like tiny emerald green rugby balls . . . so we went round Wormy's little flat where he was spending Christmas alone . . . it was pokey but he'd made the effort with a little tree and decorations and everything, and it felt pretty Christmassy and cosy . . . he put an extra bar on the fire and brought out a festive bottle of mead, which tasted like a cross between honey and old lager . . . we supped on it and worked our way through the mazzies . . . it was a very pleasant evening . . . I woke up the next day in my bed at home not knowing how I got there, covered in bruises . . . I went downstairs to the kitchen and the disapproving looks of my dad . . . when I asked him what I'd done he said he was surprised I couldn't remember standing up in Wormy's front room, telling everyone I loved them and then collapsing onto the Christmas tree that went crashing into the fireplace, taking down all the decorations poor old Wormy had painstakingly put up . . . sorry Wormy, and Happy Christmas by the way . . .

'I don't care what I take as long as its powerful' . . . this is from B, the lad who just spent £80 on a pint bottle of gloopy temazepam elixir that's like that liquid concrete stuff the doctor gives you for heartburn . . . it's proper industrial strength stuff, everyone keeps passing out after a few spoonfuls . . . one morning his cousin woke up naked and all cut up with the living room completely trashed — broken glass everywhere, hi-fi dragged off the cabinet, plants and soil all over the floor . . . he could remember hardly any of it except rolling around naked in the broken glass as if he was deranged . . . a day or two later a couple of them were slugging on it again and then went out for a drink . . . when they told me the story they couldn't even remember who they went to the pub with, but they could remember Ish taking all his clothes off, then scaring everyone out of the saloon area, then falling asleep like this:

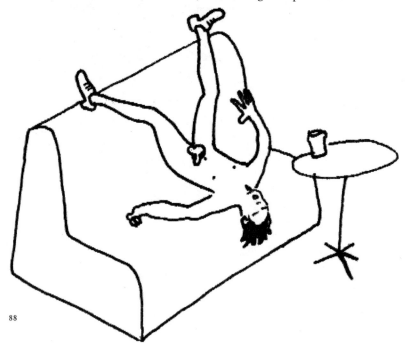

B's dad had a shadowy side to him and at his funeral the
interesting stories of his life came out, as they inevitably do . . .
the one that stuck in my mind was the incident in his occultist
friend's shed . . . B's dad was a policeman and in the course of
his daily beat he got to know a lot of people, and one of these
was the park warden who became one of his best friends over
the years . . . he'd often pop down the park, to chat, discuss
mundane matters, interesting matters, and deep, subtle matters
concerning the spiritual and the unseen . . . B's dad was naturally
that way inclined and, originally from a Gypsy background, had
converted to Islam in middle age, and belonged to the mystical
Sufi branch that produced the whirling dervishes, the holy men
who spin in a magical dance like the planets revolving around God
until they finally collapse in ecstasy . . . a town with giant monkeys
for mayors and Sufi mystics for policemen . . . and diabolists for
park wardens . . . in the best esoteric tradition the park warden
was all cagey and vague about his real beliefs but as they got to
know each other the depths of his knowledge and involvement in
secret shadowy things gradually became apparent . . . until one
day something happened and it all became shockingly obvious . . .
this was the day B's dad turned up at the park warden's special
chilling-out shed and walked in without knocking . . . the guy
was sitting cross legged, in a trance, in the nude, surrounded by
a circle of salt, on a triangle made of tinfoil, while a SIX-FOOT
GIANT OWL hovered in the murky darkness in front of him!
B's dad shat it and he swore out loud, which snapped the park
warden out of his trance, and the giant owl vanished in the blink
of an eye . . .

Mr Yull is another of my favourite dads from the Old Country . . .
once, when the summer funfair had closed for the night, with all
the usual tribal warfare between our thugs and those from the
surrounding areas, Mr Yull's daughter's boyfriend got bottled,
and the cunts who bottled him were approaching the house with
sticks and knives and whatever, and it looked like he was gonna
get completely fucked . . . but then suddenly Mr Yull barged out
of the front door, all hunched and enraged — stocky, red faced,
middle aged, like a little bull, with a mad grimace on his face
and a fuck-off antique samurai sword in his hand! There was
this tense standoff between him and the divvies with their broken
bottles and sticks . . . and then he charged them, crazy, sword in
the air, and they all legged it as fast as their chorey feet could carry
them! That was the best thing I ever saw out of my bedroom
window . . . the scene has often replayed itself in my mind . . .
and ever since then Mr Yull's been like a mythological hero
90   figure to me . . .

I never met Kermit's grandfather, but his last words stick in my mind . . . the family were gathering to pay their last respects, and as the scared thirteen-year-old leaned over the deathbed for the final time, a scrawny old hand pulled him over by the scruff of the neck so that the final wisdom could be better heard . . . and struggling and wheezing through a terrible cough, the dying voice proclaimed: 'Son . . . remember . . . keep wanking!'

I was wandering around some of the old places and my memory lingered on poor old Daddy Cool, Daddy Cool who's no longer with us, Daddy Cool who drank himself to death . . . he was a local wino who used to hang around outside the shops when I was growing up . . . the story was that his daughter had died and so he turned to drink and then he turned into Daddy Cool . . . it only occurs to me now the tragic things you can read into that name . . . the grown-ups all looked down their noses at him but to the kids he was a hero . . . we'd see him on our wanders, clowning around, falling over, livelying things up with his pissed up camaraderie . . . we'd always shout 'Daddy Coool!' in unison, and he'd raise his bottle and yodel 'Daddy Coool!' back . . . he was probably the closest thing we had to a comic book hero . . . strange to think of the real life cartoon characters that populate a child's mental landscape, pantomime characters almost, heroes like Daddy Cool or baddies like Shyanne the Bummer Man who used to hang around the toilets in the park . . .

I wanted to see my old friend S but me and S don't talk anymore . . .
we fell out a few times and in the end I just found her too hard
faced . . . but I realize a lot of that hardness of character came
from her horrible childhood, and then my feelings change
towards tenderness and regret . . . when she was a little girl
growing up in the racist Old Country of the 80s she didn't have
any friends for years and years . . . her Muslim fundamentalist
father ruled her with a rod of iron and wouldn't let her out the
house or anything so she just had to sit there with him while he
chainsmoked Lambert & Butler and obsessively read the New
Oxford Dictionary like it was the Koran . . . her one and only
relief was her comics . . . on the way home from school she'd
make a detour through the park, past the Tree Wanker, a local
character who apparently was always fucking trees, to the
towerblock where a toothless hook-nosed old man she'd never
met would bang on the window at her like a prisoner in his own
flat, and signal her over and then lower her down a stack of comic
books on a string . . . and these comics became her escape . . .
the old man she never knew was her one lifeline to a world of
dreams . . . and then one day the old man died, and that was the
end of the comics . . . and though that's not my fault, yeah, I do
wish I'd maybe tried a bit harder . . .

Luckily I still got on with K . . . she picked me up and took me to the Holiday Inn . . . she has this unhealthy habit of renting rooms at Holiday Inns and throwing herself full throttle into a fucked up self destructive bender . . . even if she's got a bed for the night . . . even if she's still in town . . . she would rather sit in the middle of the light industrial sector in a characterless, neon-lit box room with laminated hospital-style furniture and get hammered on cocaine and gin with some unlucky punter she's roped into joining her . . . I know one poor lad who went through one of these benders and then had to be up at six to sit on a coach for a 400 mile journey to Birmingham . . . no sooner had the journey begun than the person sat next to him started having an epileptic fit . . . he was delegated by the driver to look after this person for the entire journey . . . and that's the kind of crappy fallout that always follows K's little shenanigans . . .

K likes to waste time driving . . . so we drove around and took
some counter surveillance photos of the ominous military
surveillance complex on Radar Hill (the one no-one really
knows the purpose of, where strange unidentified lights fly
around, and the suits take your camera from you if they catch
you) . . . afterwards I shared a pizza with the Witch who drinks
down the pub (the Witch who works in Thomas Cook) . . . the
Witch is an idiot and seems jealous of the fact I'm K's friend and
has decided to pigeonhole me as The Hobgoblin of the Third
Mirror . . . go and work that one out . . . she was on about
forking out £250 for a real under-the-counter human skull which
she would use for magical purposes . . . diabolical purposes I
reckon . . . she claims to be a white witch but I get a distinctly
creepy vibe from her . . . there is something bad and wrong about
her . . . you feel like she's a vampiresque freak who's trying to
get inside your head and do bad things to it . . .

We spent a lot of time driving around that Christmas . . .one afternoon we got a perfect high off coke and weed and we decided to make a day of it and go out on a journey taking photos in the car . . . the combination of drugs worked so well that everything before me was bathed in poetic significance and meaning, everything seemed important and perfect, it was screaming at me to be captured for posterity on camera . . . I thought I was this classy intellectual photographer taking all these incredibly subtle and poignant shots of caravan parks and pylons, and I ran out of film early because there were just too many beautiful shots to take . . . when we got the film back, every single photo was absolutely rubbish — just pointless, badly taken, blurry snaps of ugly roadside verges and stuff . . .

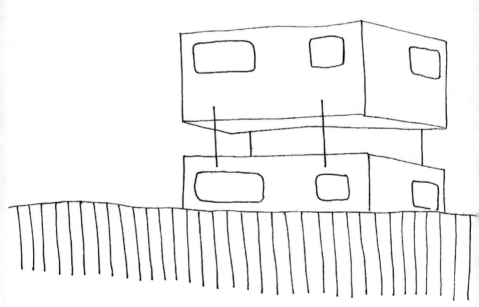

Happy days just cruising around . . . cocaine . . . McDonalds . . .
passenger seat scenery . . . everything seemed how it should be:
harmonious; simple; just right . . .

Blank pleasant Saturday
drifting round the shops
seemed happy enough

4: The New Year

The train pulls into the big smoke . . . this horrible cocaine snot slides down the back my throat . . . I stare numbly out the window at an Armageddon of cranes, bridges, motels . . . blank corporate plazas with rubble in between, sweeping vistas of commuter toytowns for the little people, the smurfs . . . I could imagine huge metallic insects looking at home here, roaming over these hinterlands . . . I feel spaced out and spooky . . . spooked out by this new order that is manifesting itself with an ever increasing intensity, spooked out by myself, by my poor old drug-addled brain and its lack of any simple warm humanity . . . it seems to take on the strange extraterrestrial quality of the scenery . . . it's a fascinating thing in its own way . . . I wish this journey could last all day . . .

It was a messy and frustrating time, that no-man's-land after Christmas, but good as well as bad . . . it was just that nothing seemed clear and I couldn't decide which direction to go . . . my mind was like the messy weather that veered from rain to sun to windy grey, from the promise of the coming warmth to dreary hopeless cold and misery, often in the same day . . . so I coasted along, taking a succession of crappy jobs, each as ugly as the next, while I tried to figure out just what it was that I was going to do . . .

I ditched the suffocation-by-office thing and decided I could never go to another temping agency again . . . next I got a job for people who don't like jobs — sitting in a cinema booth all night either bored to distraction or stressed to the point where I wanted to stab someone . . . I felt like a dog in a glass box at one of those awful petshops . . . it was in the really snooty part of town, a part of town that should be burned and looted . . . the job consisted of sitting around for hours staring at the walls and then all of a sudden taking a barrage of shit from a swarm of unbearably obnoxious Arabs and old school toffs who were clearly as nasty and arrogant as they were utterly stupid, an elite of morons incapable of doing anything for themselves, even something as simple as booking seats for a shit film . . . working near embassies and aristocrats' mansions while I was on the minimum wage, doing twelve-hour shifts and not being able to afford the five pound focaccia sandwiches over the road . . . the cinema was staffed with heavy metal students who were probably all virgins . . . they were nice enough but a shadow hung over the place in the form of the boss, a horrid little turd of a Frenchman named Guillaume with a leathery face and eyes like the Gauloises fagbutts of slow death . . . he was an asshole . . . and he paid me less than a fiver an hour . . . I didn't stay very long, but it was at least twice as long as I'd have liked . . . I hated you Guillaume, and wherever you are now you can kiss my arse . . .

Next up I got a job in a silly little grocers in the trendy warehouse area down the road . . . I walked the interview because I'd had a drunken one night stand the night before and I cruised in thinking I was Rudolph Valentino . . . the shop itself was trying to be some kind of 'concept' grocers to appeal to all the wanky web designers and fashion PRs who were bodding around buying up semi-derelict floorspace . . . it was run by this shameless estate agent who was trying to branch out and carve up his little patch of 'The New Wherever It Was' the area was supposedly becoming . . . he was an asshole too . . . or maybe it was me who was the asshole for doing all these stupid jobs . . . whatever he was he still paid less than a fiver an hour and expected me to stack shelves all day, which I suppose is fair enough really . . . I didn't see it that way though, and after a month or two I walked out of that one too . . .

London is a great place to be when you don't know what to do with yourself . . . there are loads of opportunities to look down blind alleys . . . I started attending these occult lectures and meditation sessions that were set up by descendants of The Golden Dawn in this plush ambassadorial mansion in Belgravia . . . where they got the money from I don't know, maybe they just magicked it out of their arses . . . the classes were good, but after a few weeks they suddenly just stopped and the brotherhood mysteriously vanished and I couldn't find a trace of their existence anymore . . . then I started attending gnostic classes on a Monday night up this spooky gothic turret in Holborn . . . I was up for the idea of utilizing secret knowledge and hidden powers, it seemed like a good way to go . . . they said they'd teach me how to astrally project if I stuck it out for six months . . . once I'd been to a few lessons I jacked it in though, I was put off by the fact the study notes were in unreadably bad English and the ideas they expressed were utterly feeble and air-headed . . . at the end of the day, as exciting as you want it all to seem and as much as you want to believe in it, you know deep down that they're all just full of shit . . .

On the eve of my 26th birthday I have:

*Lived in elegant mansions and pissy towerblocks
*Studied much of the world's great art, philosophy and religion, generally to a shallow coffee-table book level
*Painted some mediocre pictures
*Evaded proper work
*Met an interesting array of characters, including minor celebs, possible al-Qaeda sleepers, sex pests and wizards
*Bedded a reasonable assortment of women, e.g. Swedes, airhostesses, etc
*Been brought high and low by love
*Endured loneliness and isolation
*Been on antidepressants
*Twisted my mind on every street drug except glue
*Spoken with the spirits of the dead via occult means
*Wondered what to do with my life
*Been inspired
*Frustrated
*And bored bored BORED

I was inbetween jobs and I managed to get back to the Old Country for a few days . . . my granda had just got out of hospital, so my sister came and got me and we drove up to the Old Country to see the folks . . . driving into town, losing yourself in the place names — Foggy Furze, Little India, The Blue Lagoon . . . the first thing I noticed when we got there was that everybody drove so slow . . . people just driving, going nowhere slow . . . everybody drove like old people on a Sunday . . . up there nothing is difficult and nothing is exhilarating, life is lived with no unknowns, it all just kind of happens automatically, with little exercise of the will . . . as you arrive the suburbs and estates spread out, acres and acres of very flat, very low housing . . . a town of bungalows, a town that rarely rises above two storeys, 'A town that never quite crawls off its belly,' as a friend of mine once put it . . . the people I knew are all cruising along, having babies, turning into their dads . . . there's no hunger for anything beyond a kind of middle of the road respectability . . . a trade, a house, a phone that takes photographs . . . and I'm still bumming round London with £1.50, slying round the aisles of Sainsbury's, eating all their croissants as a free lunch and then fucking off, but I'd rather have it that way . . .

Walking into the oldies' house, the warm smells immediately
sending me back to childhood . . . the photos of all my cousins
getting their First Holy Communion with milk teeth missing . . .
my granny making a fuss as usual, with the classic, 'D'y wanna
choc ice son? I've got some jelly in the fridge,' when I'm almost
30 years old . . . I do love that little lady, and she's given nothing
but love to me . . . one of the purest, most unconditional acts of
love I ever saw was when she'd get to the end of an ice cream,
and I'd finished mine, and she'd bite it off into a little miniature
cone and put it in my tiny child's hand . . . she's a fiery one too,
which is another thing I like about her . . . she was showing us
her footy shirt that had been signed by the town team and
presented to her as a gift in recognition of her lifelong fanatical
support . . . she still goes down there at seventy-odd with a
thermos flask and a rattle . . . she even went to church in that
footy top and received Holy Communion in it . . . and that's
unusual for an old lady in the Old Country, especially a staunchly
Catholic one . . .

My granda was just taking things easy as usual, perhaps a bit more easy because he was recovering from his operation . . . but there he was as always, dreamily staring at the TV . . . if the Old Country's lazy and chilled then he's its ultimate son . . . in the war he got conscripted and just didn't bother going . . . he ignored their letters for two years until they finally came and got him . . . he worked in the steel yards afterwards where he famously installed a secret hammock so he could spend half his shift kipping . . . and that's just the kind of guy he is, a dreamy gentle man who likes John Wayne in Westerns and gets glassy eyed at newborn babies . . .

So anyway, we all sat around talking and catching up as ominous storm clouds gathered above . . . this prompted my granny to embark on a lengthy story about over the road being struck by lightning, and a lightning motif soon developed in the conversation . . . I was tired after the drive and left them with their lightning talk and went upstairs for forty winks . . . I was woken up by the crash of this almighty explosion . . . it sounded like thunder, but coming up from somewhere below . . . I don't know why this didn't make me get out of bed, but it didn't, and I started falling back asleep, until my sister stormed into the room in a right flap screaming that we'd been struck by lightning too! I woke up quickly and hurried downstairs . . . there was a big zig-zag scorch mark down the wall leading to the fireplace, and the fireplace had exploded, scattering soot everywhere, next to a half-melted TV and video . . . my mam said she saw the lightning come down the chimney as a big blue flash . . . my poor granda had been sat just in front of it as usual recovering from the operation . . . if he'd had his feet up on his pouf, well who knows what could've happened . . .

The house was in chaos . . . everyone was pacing about in shock . . .
my auntie came round . . . she had a spooky take on it because
she'd been round earlier to borrow the video but couldn't work
the leads out, and the film she'd wanted to watch was about
lightning, and how lightning melts sand into glass, but now the
video had been melted for real . . . now everyone started taking
the spooky angle, how it was weird that it was my granma's first
story of the day, and how the lightning motif had never left the
conversation, and how my mam and my granda were even
talking about it the moment it struck . . . even the fact it struck
over the road a week ago seemed ominous, because lightning
isn't meant to strike twice, which prompted my granma to quip,
'Them lot down Catcote Road get all the lottery winners, and
we get all the bloody lightning!'

As they all began to reach hysteria pitch my uncle cut through it all and holding back a smile ordered us all out into the garden . . . he pointed up at the roof, and hanging upside down off the television aerial was a really gruesome sight — a bloated, smouldering dead pigeon . . . the women groaned and the men laughed . . . this was the disturbingly comic finale of the day's events, like some kind of ridiculous omen . . . that fat grey frazzled pigeon swaying in the breeze with all of its dignity gone seemed like the ridiculous curse of a ridiculous town . . . we had a family photo in front of him, like he was our mascot, and really he was just the same as us, and all of the Old Country — absurd, graceless, just hanging around . . . but even so, I still found him funny, and in the end I still sort of liked that dead old pigeon . . .

David Brain was on the weather report earlier and he said today is the vernal equinox, the first day of spring, where for one day only there is equal day and night across the whole world . . . for some reason I'd started feeling happy again . . . London felt exciting . . . maybe the joys of spring were in my veins . . . they were certainly in the air . . . when I left the towerblock later on, the door that was jammed all winter had mysteriously decided it would start to open again . . .

Pentecost is the celebration of the Holy Spirit descending on the souls of the disciples and elevating them to ecstasy in His divine presence . . . the bank holiday Songs of Praise special was at Butlins for this year's 'Spring Harvest' Pentecost Festival . . . as one lot headed for Habitat and Matalan, another grey mass in golf jumpers and hatchbacks drove in off the bypass to praise the Lord and sing hymns . . . Butlins had got in a mystical Northumbrian folk band . . . they had Celtic drums and Aborigine didgeridoos . . . it was all atmospheric coloured lighting and accompanying dancers, and seemed to have fuck all to do with Northumbria . . . it just looked to me like spirituality as anaesthetic, completely lacking in any real spirit, any genuine vitality . . . they all looked so bloodless and dead, these Middle England Christians, their 'Pentecost Festival' looked so dreary and shit . . . but then who am I to slate their festival? I wonder, in my ignorance and cynicism, did any of this flock feel the hand of the Lord our Shepherd grace their souls, and feel the mysterious and sublime workings of the Holy Spirit come upon them like tongues of fire in that moody dry ice?

It's not often I see the dawn but when I left the house early this morning the East End skyline was soaked in delicate rosy golden sunlight . . . the streets were busy with market stalls setting up, like a scene from an age that is already long gone, and a cornucopia of fruit and veg glowed in oranges and yellows and reds in the wonderful Day-Glo sunlight . . . I forgot how impossibly romantic the dawn light can be . . . bathed in that light even these dirty old city streets look as innocent and pure as a newborn baby, and all their well-worn tiredness and sin seems washed away by its lovely newborn glow . . .

Life throws up so many passing moments of beauty and we forget nearly all of them . . . moments that seem unforgettable and perfect at the time . . . this time next week I will have forgotten that the streets were I live were awash with pink cherry blossom scattered everywhere, collecting in the curbs and drains, almost fluorescent in the golden evening sun, and I will have forgotten that for a short time at least an East End street was transformed into exotic oriental paradise . . . I will forget waking up on Neil and Lee's couch this morning, looking up at their lovely elephant mobile on the ceiling, looking for a long time, thinking a little, but not too much, stilled by the sight of the mobile, swaying gently in its way, catching the morning sun, perfect . . . sometimes, when the sun is quiet and still, I find myself staring at things for a long time, without words, in some kind of perfection and grace . . . and all these daily miracles we forget . . . but perhaps that doesn't matter; perhaps they're all essentially the same perfect moment, and we're only ever really looking at the same thing, the various reflections of the sun . . .

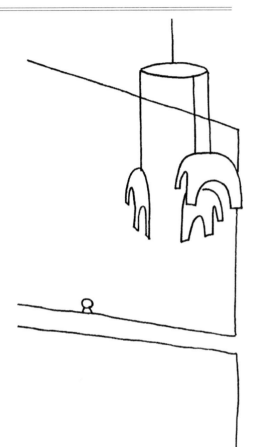

I spent most of March drunk . . . kept blanking out and waking
up for work in some foreigner's house still half cut most mornings,
slept a bit when I got in, then went back out till late. . . drank
all of my taxback and all of the rent . . . 'Happy Spring' was my
catchphrase . . . getting a job in a pub next week, which worries
me a little . . . but you only live once I suppose, and lots of
people don't even manage that . . .

5: The Pub

Enormous geological pressures create beautifully patterned crystals and minerals in the secret heart of mountains . . . the enormous human pressures of ten million people create beautiful crystals of culture and life in the secret heart of cities, crystals like this village a stone's throw from the lonely global financial zone . . . and at the heart of the village is The Pub, the place that has adopted me and many other waifs and strays, like a pissed up St Christopher carrying us over the choppy waters . . . I have to be thankful to The Pub, it's changed things for me working here . . . it's a busy, balmy Friday night, and I look down off the roof at the throng below, getting a moment's peace . . . then I climb back in through the steamy kitchen window, say hi to the freaky Thai kitchen staff, big bald Tu Tu and his gaggle of pretty ladyboys . . . and then down to the miasma of excess that swarms around the bar, an endless party, a carnival of the grotesque . . . leathery faced rag and bone men playing dominoes with models and film makers, eighteen-year-old Swedish dolly birds drugged up to the eyeballs, demented faggots stripping on tables, people dressed up as pirates . . . and I'm stood in the middle, your happy host for the evening, deranged on cocaine, sambuca, the general off-kilter vibe of The Pub, deranged on anything, good or bad, but strong . . .

If that pub had one thing, it had character . . . or should I say, it had characters . . . it had Thai ladyboy waiters swanning around fanning themselves in the heat complaining that 'Me so tired,' or 'Me so hot,' a transsexual chef, a retired bank robber, a ghost, a one-armed beggar, a Gypsy acrobat who would do back flips for money, a heroin addict who kept stealing the sandwich money, Bez, and us lot, the luckiest barmen in the world, hammered on free coke and booze, fucking Ballerinas and Brazilians and birds from Martinique, completely off the rails . . .

There is a secret and primitive power at the heart of life, I can feel its force, it's near to me, I use its power to get me sex and free drinks . . . living on a promise out here, getting by on charisma and strength of personality . . . the other day this designer gave me one of their snazzy T-shirts . . . then this posy hairdresser from The Pub offered me a free haircut, so I went round and got my haircut and had some free glasses of wine while she did it . . . then I went home and listened to my new record by this voodoo priest who knocks out deep house, which I was given by this bird from a record company I batter my eyelids at . . . I went back out with my free T-shirt and haircut and bumped into the hairdresser, and took her out for a free lunch from this cokehead chef at a trendy bar, and had some free drinks . . . then we went to a club and she bought me some more drinks and I ended up taking her home and bucking her . . . I thought I was pretty clever at the time . . . does this mean I'm turning into a twat?

Some of the women in that pub! One of my favourites is this old femme fatale who's a bit knackered now, who's been on one for far too long and has come out the other side a bit demented . . . she's got lots of stories though, like the time her brother, who ran a bar down the road, drove his car through the front saloon with her on the roof in fishnets and a miniskirt . . . the front of the pub was completely demolished but she was unharmed . . . when I asked her why she did it, she snapped defensively, 'I'm not scared of anything! I'll put fire in me mouth, I'll put drills in me mouth, I'll chew glass! I'm not scared of anything, me! The only thing I'm scared of is meself!'

There's been this right sex case coming in The Pub recently . . .
she's just split up with her boyfriend, which must have affected
her badly because she's been compulsively fucking strangers in
the bogs ever since . . . it all started one night when she got
caught giving someone a blowjob in the men's toilet . . . queues
of people started forming to watch but she just kept on going . .
. the next day she fucked two brothers in the men's toilet . . . the
men's toilet is covered in filth and sick, the cisterns overflow
onto a pissy floor, and someone has even smeared shit onto the
wall with his finger, which has become dry and cracked over
time . . . things all came to a head on Sunday . . . Sunday was
always the messiest shift of the week, the day when the weekend-
long party slid and crashed into a stinking mess and all the
mentalists who hadn't slept for two days started to gibber and
fall asleep at a bar that was soaked in dirty sticky beer . . . The
Pub looked like a Hieronymus Bosch painting on a Sunday . . .
the sex case had been drinking all afternoon and by the evening
was quite pissed . . . she'd been in the bogs with at least three or
four people by nine o'clock . . . everyone knew and people began
eavesdropping on her for a laugh . . . apparently half way through
one episode the guy's mobile phone rang, and he answered it,
mid shag, said, 'Yeah . . . I'm in the pub . . . yeah, maybe get

extra pepperoni . . . yeah . . . see you in a minute . . .' before he
finished off the job . . . a little later I saw my friend go up to the
bogs with her . . . he's married with kids . . . he'd forgotten his
wallet in a drunken stupor, and I spied his friend he'd been
drinking with all evening go through it then leave in a hurry . . .
by now I was completely sick of the whole thing . . . The Pub
seemed like the Devil's work, and we were all driving ourselves
towards our damnation faster and faster with more and more
greed and desperation, and I was thoroughly disgusted by it all . . .
when she came back to the bar, all dizzy and flushed, I found it
hard to be civil . . . I suppose I lost my temper and I told her to
fuck off out of the pub and not come back, I couldn't even look
at her I was so angry . . . and then, like a total hypocrite, I patted
my friend on the back, gave him a drink on the house now that
his money had mysteriously vanished, and tried to make him feel
better about the whole sketch . . . the sex case is now apparently
spreading her muck around Berlin . . .

The good thing and the bad thing about any local boozer is the way it becomes a little hermetically sealed world of its own . . . a world that thrives on gossip, where secrets cannot be kept . . . a case in point being the secret that Sweaty Grandad bummed Mad Michael . . . Mad Michael is a notorious sex pest and Sweaty Grandad is a painter who likes to cast himself in the heroic macho artist role, like Jackson Pollock or someone . . . apparently they'd been out on a typically debauched bender that somehow ended up becoming a furious drug-fuelled bumming session . . . it's a horrible image, to imagine them at it, their pasty, flaccid forty-year-old bodies covered in clammy sweat, liquor and drugs clogging up their smelly pores . . . the gossip spread like wildfire, and before he knew it Sweaty Grandad was mortified to be met with a wall of silence and sniggers and then the new name 'Bummer Grandad' . . . he handled it well though, and even became quite cavalier about it in the end, showing off, adding with a flourish how he'd fisted Mad Michael, but this strategy backfired when Matty pointed out that Sweaty Grandad has a gammy finger that must've got stuck up Mad Michael's arse and acted as a 'Shitclaw', which only served to fuel the hilarity further . . .

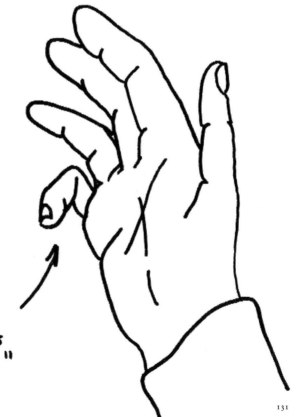

Sweaty
Grandad's
"Shitclaw"

The Pub sucks you into a world of partying that gets more and more weird the more and more blasé you become, till you end up going to parties held in transvestite brothels in the arse end of some slum . . . the crowd from The Pub ended up there one night and the trannies didn't quite know what to make of it . . . but we were all twatted anyway and we soon started getting on . . . I ended up befriending this little potbellied Welsh tranny with stubble and a Coco Chanel bob but he started freaking me out after a while, so I went for a dance with all them twisted bitches getting down to sleazy old Chicago tracks by Frankie Knuckles and Jamie Principle and the like . . . the dancefloor was in this dark neon-lit cavern . . . little corridors led off to dim rooms where sedated creeps watched porn where chicks with dicks fucked birds up the arse . . . in one room there was a cage that the little Welshman eventually climbed into and started gyrating around in . . . another room had a dungeon where they all started to congregate and after most of us lot left they apparently started working each other up until it descended into this filthy orgy . . . and after all that there is always someone's party to go to when everywhere else is shut, where everyone dances and stumbles around and gets more and more messy and demented as the sun comes up, until only the stragglers and mentalists are left . . . I remember still being round Danny's at half one on a

Sunday afternoon once with the fat chef I'd befriended and we were drinking a bottle of cooking brandy and he was sat there with a spoon washing all his coke up into rocks, and Danny was out of his mind by the window spewing this torrent of abuse at the Sunday market goers below, with taunts like, 'Hey Malteser Head, go and take your chin for a shit!', or, 'Hey Tit Head, your bird's a cunt!' to the passing policeman and policewoman . . . then you ask Gordon what time it is, and he takes off his expensive watch and he throws it on the floor and jumps up and down on it, staring you in the eye saying, 'Time's an illusion! Time's all in your mind!' and you look around the shadowy room, porn strewn across the floor, coming down off pills and crack, too weak to move, while it's a lovely sunny day outside, and though you know it's funny, you also know it's wrong . . .

I remember one day I had to throw Danny out . . . he'd been taking his duds down, showing off his pink Elvis y fronts, showing off his cock . . . then he did his 'Buffalo Bill' impression with a pint of Guinness, like so:

Which earned him a big cheer for its perfect comic timing . . . he'd been on a big bender, boozing, hammering drugs, and was fast reaching the state of delirium . . . the trouble started when he ate his first bit of food for 3 days . . . no sooner had he taken a bite of this big sweaty mushroom cheeseburger than he farts, shits himself, then falls over . . . we all agreed it would be a good time for Disco Dave to walk him home . . .

The key to a good boozer is the relationship between the regulars and the staff . . . that's what makes it feel like a local rather than a branch of Ye Olde Worlde Pubbe Co . . . I remember when one of the most regular of regulars, Little Nick, fell asleep on the stairs, and the barstaff put blankets on him and a cushion under his head . . . the weekenders who didn't know Little Nick had to walk round him on the way to the Thai restaurant in a look of disgusted bemusement . . . that pub operated on a different logic to the world outside, it flew in the face of the work ethic and the basic laws of economics . . . the staff were always late and spent the shift drunk smoking fags with the punters and half the drinks were given away for free . . . it was an island of slackness that couldn't possibly last and the rot set in when Kurt took the place over and kicked it into shape, until the spirit and the people were gone and it gradually started feeling like any other well oiled theme pub . . .

The Pub life inevitably started messing with my brain . . . I
remember doing a Sunday shift after I'd been out caning drugs
into the early hours and had gone straight to work without
sleeping . . . I couldn't communicate with anyone because I was
too paranoid they would see the twisted state I was in, but I
suppose it must have been obvious anyway . . . my mind was a
raw mass of paranoia and panic . . . the shift ahead seemed to
stretch in front of me like an unbearable endurance test . . . I
just stood there behind the bar thinking I was cracking up . . .
I kept seeing a phantom black cat prowling round my peripheral
vision . . . the door blew open and I thought I saw a supernatural
column of smoke float in and grow as if it had been summoned
here in some Faustian pact . . . as I looked on in fazed disbelief I
noticed a half empty pint on the bar grow and fill itself on its
own . . . I couldn't cope with all this but luckily my friend
Aimee was also working, and I confided in her that my head was
in bits . . . she was glad I said this because she was similarly
muntered . . . so we decided to rob a bottle of champagne from
the fridge and swig it out the back . . . from then on the morning
started flowing more easily . . . by lunchtime, after a few sambucas,
we were rolling . . . we thought we were Tom Cruise in that Cocktail
film or something . . . what a carry on; what a fucking waste . . .

I was always going to work rat arsed in those days, drinking long into the night then getting two hours' sleep and waking up on some weirdo's floor . . . smoking joints or doing lines of K just so I could get through the morning . . . one morning I felt especially fragile and had to neck a pill that was lying around just to even contemplate getting through my shift . . . big mistake because no sooner had I got to The Pub than I was completely fucked again, pacing up and down, nearly falling over, praying the boss had a hangover as usual and would not be coming in till early afternoon . . . as is often the case in this situation, weird things started happening . . . I was starting to peak and feel OK when this little old hindu guru man walked in and asked me to open my hand . . . he put a piece of paper in it and told me to open the other, and then he read my palm: 'You live till you are 89, no diseases or illnesses, you never make any money, big love around the corner, your heart is not here, soon you see opportunity and go far away . . . open other hand, think of number . . .' I thought of a number, and that was the number written on the paper . . . then the guy gave me a lucky red bead, just smiled and waddled off, leaving me completely stumped . . . I was really worried about the way I was living and what was going to happen to me back then, but this made me decide to look on the bright side . . . I thanked whoever was looking out for me up there that I didn't have Aids or cancer or liver failure . . . summer was coming up, life was peachy . . . the little red bead still sits on the windowsill and wards off misfortune . . .

It was a Bank Holiday Monday, an evil day . . . I found out later
it had been during a lunar eclipse, and the photos in the paper
showed the moon turning blood red and then disappearing into
the darkness . . . all the horoscopes spoke of 'Upsetting events' and
'Turmoil in the heavens' . . . I had been out on a three-day bender
which had involved standing on tables and doing Nazi salutes in
gay bars at eight in the morning and ended up with me lying in
bed smoking a bag of heroin on my own, which is something I
wouldn't normally do, but by that point I don't think I gave a
flying fuck anymore . . . I certainly didn't by the time I'd done that
bag in . . . by the end of it all I could do was lie on my back
spreadeagled thinking how fucked I was . . . my enjoyment was
ruined by this weird percussive African trance music blaring away
from next door keeping me up and freaking me out . . . it sounded
like a posse of them doing some weird kind of ceremony . . . I
went round in the morning with my Snoopy slippers on and
banged on their door . . . a crazy assed Somali refugee with the
eyes of a rapist murderer barged out the house and threw a
Barratt's shoe at me, ranting how he'd torture me and fuck me
in the arse then slit my throat . . . I saw a huge pile of Barratt's
shoes in his hallway and realized I'd disturbed a proper hornet's
nest . . . a few more of them piled out and I could see in their

scrawny stir-crazy faces that they were a bunch of desperadoes with nothing to lose . . . one of them twatted me expertly on the temple and I instantly went deaf in one ear . . . I stumbled around for a second then just cut my losses and legged it like a startled bunny rabbit . . . I circled the block in my damp soggy slippers and then sneaked back home . . . I was shellshocked . . . all I could think of was to lie down . . . as my head hit the pillow I saw a mad lightning flash and the sky broke into torrential rain . . . I panicked and felt like the wheels were coming off my little dream . . . everything I'd started was spinning out of control and veering off in scary directions . . . a few weeks earlier I'd been bitten in the face by a man who used to torture people for the Krays . . . as I lay there too bamboozled to think straight I just kept telling myself to be philosophical and treat these things as some kind of lesson . . .

Watching Lily Savage with her bird's nest wig hosting Blankety Blank, boxed on Special K on the sixteenth-storey of this towerblock again, reality feels a lot like this these days — off kilter, unreal, grotesquely theatrical . . . my world seems to be going off on its own a bit at the moment, and I'm scared our paths are beginning to diverge . . . living in the orbit of that pub just isn't real life . . . its like being a yellow coat at some demented resort . . . a resort that's permanently addled by booze, slags and
strong drugs . . .

Christ, that awful bloody sixteenth-storey flat . . . we spent a lot
of time up there completely goosed on Special K . . . it belonged
to a Brazilian ladyfriend of mine who's now a smackhead
poledancer . . . it was the ultimate slummy inner city cliché . . .
in the driveway there were tyres and rusty old chassis and even
just the back or front ends of cars   to get to the flat you had
to go in a lift that swayed uncertainly from side to side as it
chugged its way up to the top . . . its floor was covered in pissy
newspaper and on one occasion we even found a freshly laid human
shit . . . and once you got inside the flat there was this little
colony of Brazilians just doing loads of drugs . . . I try to recall
the evenings I spent round there but because they were mostly
on ketamine my memories are sketchy to say the least . . . but

one evening sticks in my mind, when everything came to a head
and I thought I was cracking up . . . it started off OK with me
completely battered looking out over the balcony . . . I was numb
from the neck down . . . I felt like I was levitating . . . I felt like I
was upside down . . . it occurred to me as I looked over the floating
city vista, gazing at the pigeons and getting the urge to join them,
that I maybe shouldn't be out on a sixteenth-storey balcony . . .
then I started thinking that this stupidity was typical of the way
I lived my life, and I got really down on myself and my shitty
little situation and convinced myself I was doomed . . . as the
gritty highrise skyline spread out purgatorially below me I toyed
with the idea of jumping off in a vertigoey kind of way . . . then
suddenly Mad Michael burst onto the balcony, completely naked,
also out of his mind on Special K . . . everything went tits up and
I fell into a panic attack that panned out into a long and strange
death trip . . . I sat there all night convinced my life was bound
to end soon . . . it felt like I'd irredeemably fucked it up and now
there was no way back . . . my hostess read my tarot and it was
all pain and catastrophe . . . vagrancy and fatal diseases . . . Mad
Michael turned out to be a saint that night and tried his very best
to talk me down . . . he put his clothes back on when he realized
the party was over . . . we talked about life and fate and doom
as the sun went down and came up again like some pointless
wind-up toy across the monstrous city skyline . . . and in the
slate-grey morning as I sloped off to work, I decided something
was going to have to change . . .   143

Sometimes I wonder what happened to those people, whether
they still know what day it is and are still capable of wiping
their own arses . . . I bumped into Mad Michael about a year
ago outside a late night drinking den . . . he was trying to tell me
a story while a nasty dog on a string barked away next to us,
making an unbearable racket . . . Michael got more and more
distracted trying to talk to me until he snapped halfway through
an anecdote, tore off his shirt and got down on the floor on all
fours and started shouting and snarling right in the dog's face,
even more yellow fanged and demented than the horrible rabid
animal; the dog snarled and bit and strained on its lead, and
Michael did the same, his eyes gone crazy, the veins popping out
on his neck . . . I couldn't deal with all that, and I just left him
there barking away and walked off to the next bar . . .

The last time I saw Sweaty Grandad was also very late at night . . .
he invited me to his new place, a huge disused dilapidated
factory . . . all that seemed to be in it was a solitary table and a
rusty crowbar by the door, his 'anti burglar device,' not that
there was anything there to burgle . . . it was like that filthy
room at the end of The Blair Witch Project where the man has
his back to you facing the wall . . . there was no electricity or
running water . . . we sat drinking whisky under the moonlight
till some ungodly hour . . . I was depressed at the time, almost
desperate, and this seemed like the right place for it . . . I asked
him how his life had come to this . . . he told me about his ups
and downs and about the night he went to a fancy dress party as
Big Bird and came back to find his studio burned down, and
years and years worth of paintings with it . . . there was nothing
he could do about it but sit down in the soot and flap his
feathers . . . now, with all his work gone, he was squatting a
derelict factory in a traffic blackspot . . . I asked him if he'd
regretted how his life had turned out . . . he just shrugged in
resignation and said, 'Mick, it's been vast . . .'

The Laughing Cavalier was a curious little fella who was in The Pub every afternoon, always smiling, never talking, always alone . . . he was always away in a reverie with his earphones on, and people's cruel game was often guessing what weird stuff must be coming out of them . . . one guy reckoned they just went, 'Breathe in, breath out, breathe in, breathe out , , ,' while he sat there all afternoon in some kind of moronic nirvana . . . maybe he was a bit deaf and they were a hearing aid, which would explain his lack of communication . . . I personally thought he might have been a bit mad as well and wished people wouldn't've been so mean . . . whatever was wrong he just sat there smiling and not talking all afternoon, and that's all anybody probably knew about him . . . and then one day he came in all sheepish and handed over something in a black bag, smiled shyly and left . . . he didn't say a word . . . we opened up the bag and there was this lovely naïve painting of The Pub and all its characters on a typical afternoon . . . the barstaff and the regulars and the wise old owls were all in there, so intimately observed and recognizable, as if he knew us all as friends . . . and now the painting hangs at the end of the bar and acts as a tribute to that strange, sweet man who just sat there alone and never connected with anybody, in lieu of all those conversations we never had . . .

An important thing about The Pub was that it was a boozer and not a style bar . . . it was an old gem that had grown into its present state slowly and organically, with layers and layers of history accreted and congealed into its smoke stained wallpaper and crumbling plaster . . . this was one of the things that gave The Pub its peculiar shabby glamour and drew the trendies in their droves. . . by the time I got there (i.e. too late) the place was packed to the rafters with fashionable types: stylists and fashion PRs who dressed like Kajagoogoo; Japanese photo shoots down the back alley; the children of the Home Counties in search of bohemia and inevitably settling for each other. . . but they only really surfaced at night in any numbers and by day The Pub retained a completely different character . . . the mentalists were replaced by bona-fide cockney rag'n'bone men and old timers . . . men like Buttons, who looked like Sid James and ran a sweatshop over the road . . . they'd just sit there all day drinking light ales philosophising . . . sometimes when you were especially bored they'd include you in the discussion and with a shrewd and wise look they'd tell you their thoughts like they were letting you in on an important secret, a wisdom that only ripens with age, that had been hard learned, and you in your naivety and youth were privileged to glimpse it . . . this wisdom was invariably the thickest, most lazy minded, most clichéd pile of drivel you'd ever heard . . . but then what do you expect from a bunch of old guys who've sat in a pub all day for 50 years?

Old Tom was by far and away the best of this lot and actually I'd have to admit he's a pretty special character, a true legend round those parts . . . he's one of those charismatic presences from a fading age, like a dilapidated shopfront that is just always there, giving the street its character, as you presume it will forever, but someday I suppose it just won't anymore and there'll be a gastropub or an estate agents there instead. . . he's part of the fabric of that place, Old Tom, and he stuck out like a sore thumb: a seventy-year-old rag'n'bone man covered head to toe in soot, six foot tall with hands like shovels, plastered on India Pale Ale by half three every afternoon. . . he was the only customer who drank it and we kept it in stock just for him — he'd gone through a crate a day for thirty years . . . he was the last remnant of a ramshackle era that had all but fallen away, and it was his role as a living link to a mythic East End that made him a mascot for us newcomers with our artifice and weightlessness; he guarded the pub like a totem, a guardian spirit, a badge of authenticity for the would-be urban fringe that was rapidly cannibalising itself and gentrifying away into

something far more user friendly and unremarkable . . .

Tom first arrived about lunchtime, and there was a certain mysterious and reserved nobility about him . . . after a few hours and about twelve pale ale bottles all of that went to shit and he became delirious and uncontrollable . . . on one of my first shifts I found him laughing like a slavering idiot, shouting at a fit barmaid, 'Hey, hey, ooh, I'm gonna jump over that bar and rape you! Ooh, I'm gonna fucking rape you!' . . . the barmaid just gave a knowing smile like she'd heard it all before. . . another time when he was absolutely arseholed and about to get into his van to go home, I told him he shouldn't be driving, 'What if there were little kids in the road, Tom?' I asked, 'I'll fucking kill 'em!' He slurred as he staggered off . . .

Halfway through an endless day shift and an endlessly dull conversation, some tourists walked into the pub and asked for directions, and Old Tom deliberately sent them in the wrong direction . . . when I quizzed him why he'd done this, he stared at me straight in the eye with his best enigmatic I-know-more-than-you face, and proclaimed, 'Mick, Never Help Anybody . . . never tell 'em what they need to know. . . fuck 'em . . . If you tell 'em they don't need you no more, see? Never let them know what you know.' He was on a roll now, and stopped for a dramatic pause, then drunkenly slurred, 'Mick, remember, Always Look Like An Idiot . . .' he gave me those weighty eyes again as he swayed drunkenly on his stool, his mouth slightly slavering, 'Now Mick, listen: I Claudius was the best Caesar . . . they left I Claudius alone because they thought he was an idiot . . . then they made him Caesar cause they thought he was a fuckin' idiot, and 'e'd do what they wanted . . . and then as soon they made 'im Caesar I Claudius killed 'em all!' Then he paused, to add gravitas, 'Mick, At Least An Idiot Has A Chance.' As I looked at him I thought to myself, this is the shittiest advice I've ever heard: I still think love can save the day; I still believe people are more good than bad; I'm still not scared to take a chance on life . . .   151

As I swept up the broken glass, wet fag butts and rotting vegetation, taking the usual shit from drunks and Little Hitler Kurt, I knew a better world was waiting for me, a world of sophistication and ease, a world of Kalamata olives, browsing through antique bric-a-brac, baking my own bread in Provence . . . it was clear to me that idle, balding bourgeois complacency was my birthright . . . but how was I to claim it?

6: The Dole

I eventually got fired from the pub for thieving booze . . . caught
red handed behind the bar pouring a round for me and my friends
on my day off . . . I think it was the straw that broke the camel's
back . . . so fate rolled out the red carpet once more and walked
me straight back into the Job Centre . . . if the endless intricacies
of the forms and fact that I was almost unemployable weren't
depressing enough, I had the added bonus of signing on in one
of the absolute armpits of London . . . I warn you now, never
sign on at the Whitechapel Job Centre . . . it took them three
months to get me any money and in the meantime I had to go
for an emergency loan from the Stepney SS . . . the Stepney SS is
beyond belief . . . it is the place you end up when everything else
has failed, it is the ends of the earth, the bottom of the barrel . .
. it's like the bureau where all the useless people are rounded up
before they get carted off to some unspeakable concentration
camp somewhere in 1940s Stalinist Romania . . . God, just the
smell of the place . . . the smell of beggars and junkies and the
poor Kosovan refugees caught in the middle of it all . . . the
smell and the clientele . . . I joined the enormous queue behind a
disturbed vagabond who was slumped over a can of Tennent's
Super trying to put a fag out on his nose . . . then another go-
getter staggered in with no front teeth and a forehead that was

all cut up and scabby, mumbling at no one in particular . . . two pissed-up tramps further down the queue started brawling but because they were both so out of it they fell over pretty quickly and ended up just kicking each other pathetically as they wriggled about on the floor, while refugee babies cried next to them . . . I was dumbfounded . . . it was like being trapped in a Victorian nuthouse . . . it was like the Whitechapel of Jack the Ripper or The Elephant Man . . . I just tried my best not to get noticed . . . I was powerless to do anything but wait, and wait, and keep waiting . . . it took them five hours to get me my emergency giro, five hours in the worst place in England . . . I was shaking when I left, traumatized, soiled, brought low . . . I had to purge it all from my mind, and within an hour I had cashed the giro and was goosed on a bottle of rosé and six co-proxamol, watching the cricket on Channel 4 with one eye involuntarily shut, like a poncier version of all the other vaggers from the Stepney SS . . .

I love waking up at one-thirty, just in time for Quincey, with a fuck-off muggy headache, sleep crusting my eyes, snot clogging up the very back of my nose that I can never quite get rid of, swollen sinuses, itchy scalp, no energy and my left trouser leg damp with cold piss . . . this is when the world is truly my oyster and I know I am an unstoppable winner . . .

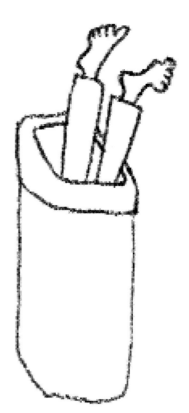

I was walking back from another of my pathetic job hunts . . .
the weather was dour and oppressive and I felt any positive
attitude collapsing into depression and my mind sinking back to
that dark cobwebby place I don't like it to . . . as I looked out
across the dreary skyline I noticed that the Gherkin and the
Natwest Tower and even the good old Truman chimney all
seemed to be beginning to lean slightly and would soon end up
like the tower in Pisa. . . I worried the whole foundation of the
London clay must be going the same way my head was and I
panicked and scuttled home quicker . . .

My mind was still in that cobwebby attic place a few days later when I was looking in the mirror trying to get out of the house that afternoon . . . to my utter horror I noticed for the first time that my eyes are completely wonky . . . they looked like this:

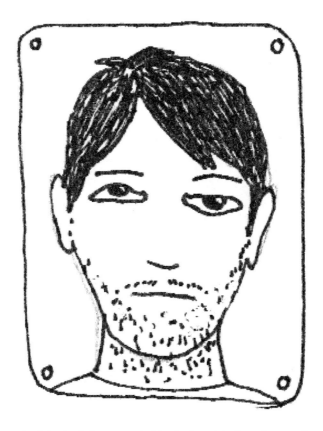

Not only did I look bong eyed, I looked positively subnormal . . . well, that ruined my confidence and my plans for that day. Still no job.

I was in a real pickle here: every angle and option seemed as horrible and pointless as the last one . . . I couldn't bear another McJob — people kid themselves there's something worthy about an honest day's toil slogging away for peanuts but we all know really there isn't, is there? I always remember Tony telling me about his job as a builder going up and down flights of stairs with back breaking concrete slabs all day, and I asked him, 'But doesn't it make you feel like a hero?' and he answered, 'No mate, it makes me feel like a fucking dick . . .' I didn't want anything resembling a career either, didn't want to start at the bottom and work my way to middle management, running around like some muppet in a cheap shirt and tie . . . but most of all I didn't want to be an unemployable loser, a bitter loser stubbed out on the fag butt of society with all the sociopaths and slobs with their Saint George flags hanging out of their council house windows . . .

I started keeping a notepad and writing it all down . . . it was like writing became a battle against myself and against the dole . . . some kind of proof I wasn't just a wanker who was so useless he couldn't even get along in one of the world's strongest economies . . . justification for the fact I'd never given the idea of anything resembling a career a second thought, that I was just incapable of it . . . there was always the nagging thought that maybe I should be a bigshot in advertising or some other horribly slick and professional arena but when it came down to it the only kind of job I ever applied for was a bus conductor or a miniature train driver . . . I'd always felt like this was a good thing rather than a bad thing, but life seemed to be saying otherwise . . . I began to dread turning into that middle-aged loser in a bedsit who'd somehow missed the bus and was just stuck there forever . . . living in doss holes, eating bad food, settling for Pizza Hut as your occasional meal out, learning to live with spontaneous violence and burglary, never getting the fit birds . . . and slowly the writing began to seem like a last chance saloon to stop this inevitability from coming true . . .

I would do my best to drag myself out of the daily quagmire by forgetting about jobs and losing myself in writing and vast meandering walks . . . each day became a pointless and enchanting bittersweet wander through the city, cut loose from all concerns out there on a shoestring, in my world of notebooks, crisp butties and giro sightseeing . . .

I solved the main problem of giro tourism — the expense of eating out — by regressing into a diet of kid's snacks . . . the regression into childlike financial dependence and childlike spending power seemed like a fair trade-off for the childlike expanse of playtime before me . . . I could get a whole day out of circumnavigating London Fields to Stokey on £1.50 . . . looking at all them cows' hooves and chicken claws in the shanty town shacks of Ridley Road Market happy as Larry on two bags of Spaceraiders and a Wham Bar . . .

My meanderings always seemed to take me into nasty areas . . .
I was drawn to them like a fly round shit . . . I would get scared
when I started noticing the piles of tyres and rusty engines and
Le Corbusian labyrinths, and imagine the little bastards in Gap
hoodies wanting to mug me . . . but then I'd laugh in relief to
myself when I realized I only had 12p on me and nothing worth
mugging . . . it was like my poverty guaranteed me my absolute
freedom, gave me the keys to the city . . .

Everything changes when you've got nowhere to go . . . your attitude to buses for example . . . one day the 242 stopped next to me as I ambled down the road and I decided to just jump on and stay on and see where it took me . . . I realized I'd been treating the bus all wrong: I'd only ever used it as a means of getting somewhere, like work or the shops on my day off . . . I loved the bus anyway, I always rushed to the front seat on the top deck like an excited tourist . . . buses evoked that basic sense of touristic romance about London for me . . . but now I wasn't going anywhere, whole new vistas of possibility were suddenly opening up, and I realized I could lose myself in a top deck reverie all day and it would only cost £1 there and £1 back . . . the journey took hours as you crawled and grinded deeper into the maze, but this was all part of the pleasure . . . what was previously a frustration became an added bonus . . . you could waste an entire afternoon on your expedition . . . it gave you time to enjoy the scruffy mysteries that unfolded lazily before you . . . Saxon clocktowers underneath Victorian bridges for Jules Verne steam trains that land in the moon's eye in that famous silent film; grim and monolithic Orwellian hospitals; gypsy camps on traffic islands underneath motorway flyovers; stretches of dirty derelict countryside; mucky industrial rivers I never even knew existed . . . though the distances covered were trivial, the journeys were immense . . . epic distances compressed into a few magnificent square miles . . . space telescopes in on itself in the labyrinth of London, its absolute gravity warps and shrinks space like a black hole, until it becomes impossible to achieve escape velocity, and all life is trapped here forever in these infinite square miles, these heroic maze-like streets that are the streets of life itself . . . and though my budget was £3.50 I felt privileged to be here watching it all unfold before me like a beautiful giro road movie . . .

I must admit, I kind of liked signing on in a way, I liked the
freedom it brought, a strange solipsistic kind of freedom . . .
not having any structured contact with other people like you do
when you work, not having enough money to participate in
society and its activities, which is largely based on some kind of
consumption or transaction of cash, I felt like I hardly qualified
as a citizen anymore in any practical sense, I'd been pushed
outside the loop, and I quite liked being on the outside looking
in . . . one day I was heading back home over London Bridge . . .
I was swamped in the rush hour tide of suits and secretaries
flooding away from the City against me . . . a deluge of worker
bees heading home . . . I stood to the side for a minute just to
watch them all marching on unflinchingly, and not one single one
of them looked up at me, they just pushed onwards obliviously,
locked into the rhythms of working and commuting and the
banality of their lives and probably their dreams . . . or at least
that's how it looked to me, all bitter and insecure, scabbing
about with 70p in my pocket trying to walk against the tide . . .
I don't know if I was any better but wherever the truth lay, I
was still glad I wasn't walking the other way . . .

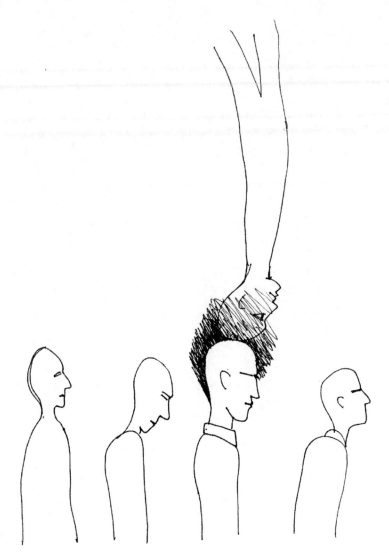

One day I was right up the top of Highgate Hill with the crickets and the dragonflies, looking down over the sprawling heaving monstrosity below . . . it shimmered under its own smoggy heat . . . you could still feel the low vibration of the traffic . . . a wood pigeon came by my bench and I noticed how beautiful and healthy it looked — its clean, pretty plumage, its well fed size — and then I thought about the ugly urban pigeons down there in the valley below, where the whole machine grinds to a standstill under its own terrible pressure and weight, where all the filth and scum accretes, and people want to murder you . . . I thought about the city pigeons' scrawny necks and filthy feathers, their hobbly stumpy feet, and I imagined what the city down there must be doing to you and me, and then I envisaged it all suddenly going up in fire and brimstone like T2 or 9/11 . . . I stayed up there a long time unwilling to move and eventually the inevitability of having to come back down gave me a sinking sense of dread in my gut . . .

We decided we'd form a band. It seemed like a great idea at the time . . . I thought I'd drop in on an old pal of mine and that day fate took a hold and threw us into a heroic arena where we both instantly became legends in our own minds . . . he lived over West and I'd followed a strange instinct that day and decided to take up a challenge I'd thought about a few times — walking from the East End to the Portobello Road along the canal, an epic journey that would join up lots of dots along the way that I didn't really know about yet . . . my day assumed an epic quality as I trekked along the superhighway of the industrial revolution, through the patchwork of mini-states that is London, with their contrasting suite of minor moods: London Fields with its boho bicyclists and dilapidated gasworks; Hoxton looking strangely pastoral with its quaint little sweatshops and smokestacks under the broody sky; Islington proud and impressive with its designer lofts in massive old chocolate factories; Kings Cross all irredeemably sad and bleak and mossy and intriguing; Camden shamelessly tarted up with enormous papier-mâché Doc Martens for the crappo Germans in ethnic hats; Regent's Park exquisitely elegant and the Zoo with its zebras and pelicans; Lord's, Little Venice, Paddington Basin, Westbourne Park, until finally alighting at the magnificently ugly Trellick Tower, Ernest Goldfinger's brutally elegant Stalinist towerblock, like the towerblock that would have been reserved for the Soviet cosmonauts, a slim concrete finger pointing skywards to a future that never was . . . by the time I got there I was fucked . . . as I stepped off the canal I had the sealegs of a sailor who'd just stepped ashore . . . my arse was chaffed and every step was a small agony . . . I walked up the path like Charlie Chaplin wondering how to get to D's . . .

172

I phoned him up to find out how to get to where he lived . . . it was a surprise visit but by strange and wonderful coincidence he said he'd just started setting some of my writing to music and he thought it was a fateful opportunity for us to start working on this new idea . . . he told me to get straight over . . . D lived in the hinterlands of this area, out past the goods yard and the cemetery, and by the time I found his house he'd already got a basic track down . . . I was starving, and he took me to the kitchen, a pokey affair, and only had bread or Nutella . . . I said I'd have some plain bread and I noticed on his piece he spread three spoonfuls of sugar with his finger . . . his room was as bare and sad as you might expect, but there were big branches he'd found on the street up against the walls and I noticed a copy of Machiavelli's The Prince on the table and a picture of Michael Heseltine from a Sunday supplement bluetacked onto the wall . . . I can do business with this guy, I thought to myself . . . as I sat down and relaxed with a cup of tea and listened to the music my sprawling ridiculous day began to finally feel vindicated . . . I became very excited . . . the laptop track was beautiful, a marvel . . . it suited the words perfectly, made them ten times better . . . as we talked cornucopias of possibility began to overflow: record company expense accounts; banging models; the mile high club; hanging out with foreign film directors; doors opening to members' bars in ridiculously sophisticated capitals all around the world . . . I think at that moment we suddenly became legends in our own imaginations, and we were so fired up we stayed up working and talking till it got light again . . .

We had every reason to be excited, it was our one chance to escape our destiny of staying losers all our lives, and what a pair of losers we felt like . . . at that point neither of us were even allowed bank accounts, that most basic of modern needs, like running water or shelter — forced outside the circuit of modern society, no longer fully fledged citizens . . . the people who couldn't get along in the strongest economy in the world . . . educated young men from decent backgounds trapped between the dole and the worst jobs in the world, the jobs reserved for people who can't speak English, the jobs where you have to work nights, the jobs where you have to work Christmas . . . after years doing the jobs nobody else wanted, or not even getting them, our hearts just weren't in it anymore . . . D wasn't working then but on his last attempt to get a job he did a trial shift at a trendy faux-cockney sausage and mash restaurant; the shift was unpaid, busy and eight hours long, and they wouldn't even give him a free sausage at the end of it . . . with odds like these the dole seemed like the only realistic alternative — that is, until that fateful day . . . I fell asleep drooling over our future Club Tropicana lifestyle and woke up on the hard floor with my clothes all twisted round back to front in the freezing cold pokey flat . . . I felt rough . . . D seemed to live on a diet of Nutella and Marlboro Reds so that was what was for breakfast . . . it seemed wrong for two guys getting on for thirty to be living like this, but the dream of the Club Tropicana lifestyle made it all seem like garnish, transitory detail of no consequence . . . of course, this didn't turn out to be the case, but for a day and a night there we were, magnificent and invincible: two losers who couldn't even afford to charge their mobile phones; two legends with our hands round the throats of the music industry . . .

7: East of Essex

I decided what I needed was a little break, just to try and muster up some kind of inspiration, so I called my friend and invited myself out to her home in Essex . . . Essex might not be the first choice for a holiday destination, but I was stony broke and it was only up the road . . . I always presumed Essex was pretty boring, but I was taken on a twisted magical mystery tour and found out it is one of the strangest places you could ever imagine . . .

The train journey was interesting enough in its own way . . . from the corporate colossus of Liverpool St, past the Gherkin squatting there like some draconian extra-terrestrial power, we glided through the old East End and its slummy riches and transition from post-Blitz squalor to ecological parks, style bars and Victorian hat factories being converted into trendy distressed-brick lofts . . . beyond this inner circle as London diluted into the boredom and sprawl of pebbledashed rows disappearing into the distance, followed by hinterlands of flyovers and light industry with a spectral, otherworldly quality . . . the tensile steel structures of hi-tech retail parks and Holiday Inns bathed in neon beneath the cold magnificence of the stars . . . it occurred to me that this is how Lunar colonies will look . . . Mars will have McDonalds and Holiday Inns . . . the future is already coming to pass, on Earth instead of Heaven, scattered across the roadside, in the places we drive thru on the way to somewhere else . . .

I met C at Wickford station . . . she wondered if I was ready for
our journey into 'The Heart of Darkness' as she put it rather
archly . . . but first we had to go to the local retail park, because
our mission apparently also involved 'exorcising the demons of
the new town' . . . we stopped at Petworld to pick up some
dogfood . . . there was a fat, fifty year old skinhead in the queue
with a tattoo of his Alsatian's face on his forearm . . . this is kind
of how I'd always imagined Essex: cockney overspill, Mike Reid,
Romford Dog Track, catalogue Thai wives, cocaine, Car Phone
Warehouse . . . our mission, I was informed, was to drive east of
this Essex, deep into the forgotten marshland peninsula, into the
heart of English witchcraft, into six-toed Essex, uncle-fucker
Essex, the scary badlands of the crazed backwoodsman . . .

Just past The Café, a late night illegal gambling den and National Front HQ, we stopped for a cheeky half at the last outpost before this other Essex, C's local, The Prince of Wales, and that was strange enough . . . the characters of The Prince of Wales included the Coldstream Guardsman, who spent most of his military career in solitary confinement, who salutes the Queen and then the sky every night as he leaves; Ivan the one-legged Gypsy who is barred from the other pub after taking his poaching gun to its landlord; Manos, the cocaine addict chef who lives in a circus wagon out the back; Stitch, the half East End, half Gambian Hell's Angel who looks like a Maori warrior, who once slept in the local cemetery and woke up with a dead baby's head between his legs . . .

We had one for the road then resumed our mission, east of Essex proper, into the Denjy . . . the Denjy is the marshland peninsula famous for 'marsh madness', a form of malaria . . . I was coming down with flu and was starting to feel quite feverish and strange by now, and started tucking into the provisions I'd brought: an expensive bottle of Armagnac XO and some Caring Clowns, these child's eucalyptus lollies, and as we drove deeper into that shithole, dissipated and drunk, I fancied I was some consumptive or tubercular dandy from a more pretentious era . . .

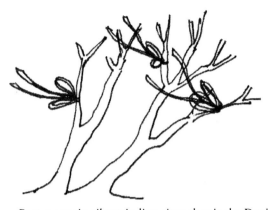

Past a certain silty winding river that is the Denjy's natural border, the night drew in, the roads got narrower and the fog came in thick and low . . . the stars assumed a strange aspect out there, the constellations looked bright but unfamiliar and askew . . . Orion watched twisted and strange above this misty, insubstantial realm we were entering . . . we rolled on with the fog past mock-Tudor prefabs, past a shop with the sign, 'Watch out, watch out, Gypsies about,' past the bungalow of C's witch friend, where all the ley lines converge, and C swears she once saw a non-human dwarf creature dressed in leather and furs manifest itself in the corner of the room . . . she offered to pop in but I firmly refused . . . the fog induces a strong feeling of unreality, of a dreamy world still being formed . . . I was beginning to feel pretty feverish by this stage . . . I spotted some ribbons tied to a tree in the road, apparently a common magical practice in these parts . . . an ancient Templar chapel waited next to a nuclear power station . . . all the while C fed my imagination with tales of Wiccan communities living wild in the woods somewhere outside Braintree, or a bunch of illegal Kosovan refugees who hijacked a van and went AWOL, disappearing out into the marsh, never to be seen again . . .

The foggy marsh got less and less real, more and more Brothers Grimm as we approached the epicentre of all this weirdness, the ancient town of Canuden . . . Canuden, the seat of King Canute, and the place where Matthew Hopkins the Witchfinder General burned his 3,000 witches . . . its awful history stays in the air, pollutes the aethyr, comes back threefold to haunt the Denjy, comes back by drawing the town's 9,000 inhabitants to it, a catalogue of human detritus: inbred natives, villains running away to the ends of Essex where people will stop looking for them, fucked up weirdos caught in the sick romance of devil worship and paganism's dark side, using them as an excuse for sadism, kiddy fiddling and whatever other filth they get up to . . . a new age dystopia, a sick flipside to places like Rosslyn or Glastonbury . . . like C said, why would you come to Canuden unless you were fucked up?

The omens on the way to Canuden were ominous enough . . . a static caravan community with 'The Dome Village' written on the big caravan at the entrance . . . the Gypsy village where the King of the Gypsies lives, and they shoot at you if you try to go there . . . a huge barn that had been smashed and upturned as if it were a child's toy . . . what kind of force could do that? Beyond the barn Canuden church watched through the fog, dominating the landscape from its hillside, giving off bad vibes . . . I was gripping the seatbelt and my bottle of Armagnac very tightly by that point . . . Canuden church wasn't signposted, there was no tourist information plaque or even a sign outside bearing its name . . . it was a church that tried to have no history, to melt into insignificance, yet it was surrounded by spiked railings and monitored by CCTV; how many village churches do you know that need spiked railings and CCTV? We cautiously got out of the car . . . a tangibly nasty feeling was thick in the air . . . there were more of those fucking ribbons in the trees . . . a medieval cross commemorating the atrocity had been defiled with its head upside down on the grass . . . I'd had enough of that place and wanted to get the fuck out of there, but I had the sinking feeling I was now infected with its atmosphere, and there would always be a little bit of Canuden in me, or a little bit of me in Canuden, which is really just the same thing anyway . . . we decide to resume our quest and continue into the Denjy until we hit the eastern seaboard, the end of the road . . .

Out past Canuden there was even less . . . the badlands thinned out until they were only boggy marsh, a fog that rolled out all the way east, and a single, dangerous winding road that went on for miles . . . I had the fevery fancy that maybe this floating, misty world was really the breath of a hidden and terrible creation deity, and thirty miles away in London it had solidified and crystallized into the Gherkin and the Natwest Tower, but out here it was more and more primitive and breath-like as we drove closer and closer towards its Genesis: a set of horrible, gaping, divine jaws . . .

At this point, our journey to the ends of Essex was cut short . . .
we saw the foglights of a car stationary and suspicious in the
road up ahead . . . as we slowed we spied two sinister old
women in the car looking at us funny, like they'd been waiting
there for us for some horrible reason . . . the next thing we knew
we jerked forward and stalled with a big splash and were half
submerged in a flooded road! It was as if the Denjy, like King
Canute in his battles with the tide, had finally given up, and
reverted back into the primordial, half formed world of the fog
and the sea . . . we panicked . . . what the fuck were the two old
women doing waiting out here? Luckily the battery held out and
we managed to reverse out of the flood and not find out . . . I
looked at the old women as we struggled to escape and they held
my gaze with evil stares . . . then in an instant they turned all
their lights out and disappeared into the foggy darkness . . . we
did a u-turn and got the fuck out of there as quickly as possible,
away from Canuden, away from the Denjy, back to the relative
civilization of Mike Reid, catalogue Thai wives, cocaine, Car

Phone Warehouse . . .

Once we got back I realized I was getting seriously ill . . . I soaked the bedsheets through about four times that night . . . I lay there all feverish in my friend's gingerbread cottage scared of a shadowy Quaker spectre I imagined waiting by the window over the road that C had christened Devril . . . I also sensed a closer more miasmic force floating over the bed ready to suck the breath out of me . . . I was in and out of troubled dreams all night . . . at the crack of dawn C's parrot started reeling off an endless stream of 'Hello! Hello! Hello!'s, which set off the super nervous and excitable Weimeraner, who bounded up the stairs and ran round the cage barking and trying to eat the parrot . . . I hid my throbbing sweaty head under the wet pillow . . . five minutes later the worst pain I ever experienced hammered into my chest . . . it was like being strapped to a table and having your upper abdomen crushed in a vice while a torturer had discovered the sport of continually dropping an anvil on top of your ribcage . . . I was bundled into the car with the usual indignity that accompanies a sick man: I'd fallen over on the bathroom floor and soaked my trousers, so I put a pair of C's jogging bottoms on, which were too big and kept falling down, revealing my cock . . . I was bundled in the back of the Beetle and we sped off to the nearest general hospital . . .

For someone doubled over in excruciating agony I'd hardly say they broke a sweat . . . it took ages to even see anyone, and then they sauntered around for a bit with a stethoscope, and then they left me on the bed to 'relax' and look up at an electric lightbulb, beside myself with pain . . . then they'd come and do a blood pressure test or whatever, no rush . . . they didn't even give me any decent painkillers, just tried to palm me off with paracetamol . . . by now I was giddy and had pins and needles with all the pain . . . after pestering them for a long time they finally gave me something half decent that eased it off a little . . . in the meantime they tried to take a simple blood test and fucked the needle up five times in a row . . . I hate needles anyway and they made a right mess of my arm below the wrist . . . then they fucked up my mainline vein and ruined my new white deck shoes as a steady rivulet of black blood flowed all over the sheets and the bed and onto the hospital floor . . . at least it took my mind off my chest for a while . . . they told me they were concerned and wanted to keep me in overnight . . . the pain had got to a manageable level and they zipped me off upstairs in a wheelchair . . .

I thought my situation might improve but they just put me in another room that was much the same, just far more depressing with far sicker people . . . there was a delirious woman with gammy legs in the bed opposite mumbling 'You got a lovely little baby . . . is he called Christopher your baby? You got a lovely little baby . . . I used to have a little baby too . . .' and so on, to no one in particular, all night long . . . I winced on the bed while I waited for the doctors to come and talk to me . . . it took them till two in the morning . . . I nagged and nagged but it soon became clear to me that this was going at their pace, a disgraceful pace, but I was powerless to do anything about it, I was just a cog in the hospital machine . . . in the meantime they wouldn't even let me check into a proper bed where I could get away from the bright electric light . . . I got up and shuffled to the deserted TV room . . . I turned the lights off and opened the window and sat and watched a heavy magnolia moon in the darkness, the one thing in my sensory range that wasn't completely doing my head in . . . the doctors finally saw me and put me to bed, and among the chronic snorers I finally got some sleep . . .

When I woke up I felt pretty good . . . the pain was gone and I was glad I could finally get out of that awful frustrating place, a place where no one seems to care about you and you must keep trudging slowly through the motions just to move forward a little . . . I was all ready to sign myself out on a release form, when suddenly I started to shiver and shake so violently that the bed began to squeak like a naughty speeded up Benny Hill sketch . . . then there was this almighty crash as the old guy next to me fell out of his bed and onto my table and lay there moaning on the floor . . . I couldn't see what was going on because there was a curtain in the way but I could smell this really thick fertilizer-like diarrhoea smell . . . this panicked me and the chest agony kicked back in with a vengeance . . . again I had to start pestering the nurses and again they swanned around doing bugger all about it . . . I lost my temper and started barking orders at them because I realized what a disgrace they were and what a serious position I might be in and I knew it was the only way I'd get anything done . . . ten minutes later I had stripped off and was sweating buckets and burning up really badly . . . I demanded they get me some proper medical attention . . . they said things like, 'Could you put some clothes on Mr. Smith?' I said things like, 'No, I'm burning up you idiot! And get me some fucking decent painkillers this time!' Eventually the doctor came and told me I was quite seriously ill and definitely wouldn't be leaving for quite a while . . . this was really depressing news: seriously ill and stuck in that trap indefinitely . . . but at least they finally got the morphine out . . . they injected it into the rump of my arse like I was sick cattle or something and shortly after I drifted off with the relief of it all . . .

I woke up alone and dreamy in a white room with clean dry sheets and a ridiculous white dress on . . . the gentle sunlight made shapes on the walls . . . it was still and quiet at last . . . nothing but the sunlight and the white walls and the slow drip-drip of the various bags of fluid that were now feeding into a tube that was hanging out of my arm . . . the drip marked a gentle, circular kind of time, where nothing happened and things just went slowly round and round . . . I felt very nice indeed . . . if I couldn't get out of hospital I didn't mind staying like this at all . . .

But of course it couldn't last . . . I was only in that room because
they thought I might have Hepatitis, which is infectious, but I
didn't . . . I had two dirty gallstones that had got blocked in my
pipes which had led to a serious septic gastric infection . . . that's
why I was sweating so much and it stank of piss and why I was
turning waxy yellow . . . the agony in the chest was hypertension
and the build-up of acidic bile . . . the doc told me an older man
would've lasted three days then snuffed it, but that's just me
showing off . . . anyway, they put me in the gastric ward, and that
means the ward that has to deal with a steady slurry of shit . . .
everywhere in that ward there was the constant background smell
of varying degrees of rancid shit, or the dubious disinfectant
smells of shit trying to be covered up . . . other background
notes included the sounds of constant snoring and farting, the
hum of industrial scale extractor fans just outside the window,
and an old voice moaning 'Help . . .Help . . .Help . . .' exactly
the same for hours and hours every night . . . my immediate
neighbours were an old man called John with big tubes coming
out of his stitched-up stomach, who lay on his back every moment
of the twelve days I was there and generally dozed and snored
but occasionally woke up and said things like 'Oh, please God,
please just let me die,' and meant it . . . there was also Joe, who
hardly seemed to sleep at all, who just sat in his chair at all times
and stared with creepy zonked-out eyes . . . at night he'd use this
oxygen inhaler that sounded like the Prince of Darkness hissing
in the shadows and you'd look over and he'd still be in his chair
but in the darkness you couldn't be sure if he was looking at you
or not . . . the idea of having to stay in that place indefinitely
just broke my spirit after a while . . . you finally realize you're
not going anywhere and you can't do anything but try to relax
about it and ride it out . . . at least the morphine helped . . .

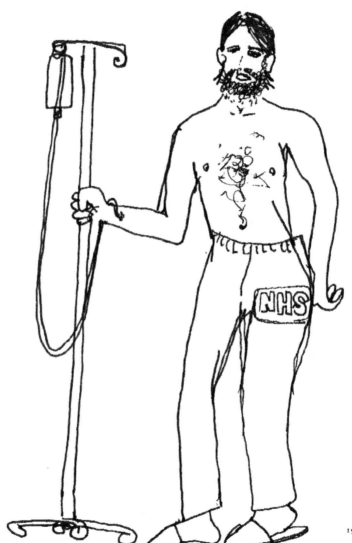

A week into it, I had to get out and I slipped away from the horrors of the shitters' ward when the nurses weren't looking and escaped into a quiet sunny morning in the suburbs of some strange Essex town . . . it was as completely alien to me as I must have been to the curtain twitchers watching me shuffling around in my apple green NHS pyjamas and slippers, with my glazed eyes, yellow complexion and massive square beard I'd developed . . . I must have looked like a cross between Charles Manson and a Muslim extremist, come to burst their soporific little suburban bubble . . . I swayed through the cul-de-sacs out of my mind on morphine and I think at that moment I was the happiest man in Essex . . . I could smell cut grass instead of shit and Dettol and hear crickets and birds instead of ventilators and screams . . . it was the first time I'd felt the effects of the morphine outside the context of suffering and degradation and the first time I truly appreciated the subtle sensory pleasures and fairytale quality of the drug . . . it felt how waking up from blissful slumber must feel for a little baby . . . a warm bath of soft sunlight for the senses . . . I felt a little paranoid and out of place so I hid away from the Neighbourhood Watch crew . . . no one was going to take me away, I said to myself . . . I found a little hidden bit of sun-dappled green and sat down on a tree stump with these furry toadstools growing out of it . . . I wondered when the big spider would turn up looking for Miss Muffit . . . I could hear a ridiculous woodpecker hammering on a nearby tree . . . I don't know if you've ever heard one but it sounds just like it would do in a wacky 50s cartoon . . . I was so happy . . . the slow hiss of the old people's cars drifting past at a leisurely thirty lulled me into a kind of bliss . . . after that ward, suburbia seemed like paradise . . . or more precisely, it seemed like a suburb of paradise, not the really good bit where the Tree and the Snake and all the action was but the outer edge where all the boring unremarkable Edeners who'd never go near that scandalous apple in a million years could just drive around at thirty and hang

perpetually in the amnesiac bliss between here and eternity . . .

The operation to get the gallstones out went well but they kept
me in a couple of days more . . . I was glad I was OK but after
two weeks I was desperate to get out of that place . . . the people
and the dynamic just made me sick . . . the Olympics, irony of
ironies, was on when I was in hospital, and all the old blokes
who could hardly walk huddled into the telly room in their
pyjamas watching pole vaulters and hundred meter breast stroke
champions with glazed eyes . . . everyone just sleepwalking
through the horror of it all, accepting it; they were the old and
the dying, the people with no fight left, or just the general losers
with no fight in them in the first place, the fat smokers with bad
diets who just put up with their plight, in hospital and in life,
the passive and accepting victims of whatever life dished out at
them . . . it struck me the victims of the hospital machine were
very similar to the victims of the giro machine or the Stepney SS
or the world of shit jobs . . . a person thinks about these things
when he's stoned on morphine and has nothing to do for two
weeks . . . a person thinks about a lot of things . . . before that
I'd never really thought much about death . . . here you could
feel it lurking in the crevices, where they tried to mask it with
the stink of disinfectant . . . I saw people die in there, saw their
families huddled round a bed, saw that bed freshly made
afterwards, all clean and strange and empty . . . I realized in that
hospital that death is close: it waits in stairwells and beds and
cars; waits at the bottom of bottles of wine and the thighs of
beautiful women . . . death is always close, and for life to make
any kind of sense it must be lived as a kind of two fingers up to
it, must be brave and strong and alive . . . and I vowed to myself
in that hospital bed that living the way I was just wasn't good
enough for me anymore, that if even a nurse wasn't going to take
care of you properly then no one ever was, and to get what you
actually wanted from life you had to get used to exercising your
own force and willpower to make your wishes real, just like
willing yourself well and getting out of the hospital situation . . .

I didn't want my life to be like being in hospital, I didn't want to be waiting in a metaphorical wheelchair in a comedy dress for someone to come along and change my pissbag wrong and then just fuck off and leave me to it, I didn't want to go down the Stepney SS anymore and drown my dignity for an £80 cheque, I didn't want to sit in a cinema box and I didn't want to humour drunks . . . I didn't want to leave anything in the hands of anyone else, like bosses or dole offices or nurses, because they are only as half-alive as their slowly dying patients, dulled by hospital culture and the essentially passive role they've played in the unfolding of their own lives . . . I'd always wanted life to be magical and beautiful and alive, but I realized I'd been trying the wrong way to get it like that . . . I'd always thought it'd just come to me if I fended off careers and ambition and humdrum soap opera things . . . I had the idiot notion that eking out a tenner over three days by living on Space Raiders somehow made you holier, like some phoney Buddhist rubbish . . . I realized in that hospital bed that the meek aren't blessed and they aren't going to inherit bugger all, and if you wanted poetry you were going to have to pull your finger out your arse and write some down . . . I'd laboured under the lie that I could live like some kind of playboy, just one with no money, that nobility was a thing of the mind, and the money and means side of it would disappear if you denied its existence completely enough . . . but now I realized a playboy floats along weightlessly just as much as a bum does and in the end living like a giro playboy amounted to fuck all anyway . . .

Being honest with myself, I knew I wasn't going to get what I
wanted through the kind of hard work people do in jobs: that is,
working as a means of achieving something else, such as promotion
or accumulating credit . . . the kind of work I wanted to do
would have to be something I found meaningful — it would
have to be an end and a joy in itself . . . the only work I'd ever
found to be like this was art: art would have to be my Trojan
Horse, because art, like cricket or cooking or doing the garden,
is work as pleasure, work as play, which is the only kind of work
I could imagine myself being any good at . . . so I promised myself
in that hospital bed that there was a book buried somewhere in
all those years of shit jobs and signing on, of ending up in ropey
situations and glimpsing the nugget of beauty inside them, and I
promised myself that writing it all down was the only way I'd
ever get myself better and earn myself a ticket to check out of
life's general hospital . . .

I had some good news when I got back to London . . . I'd been
applying for loads of jobs and it looked like I'd landed the best
one . . . I ended up in one of the big galleries as the guy you see
sitting on the chair with the polyester uniform on telling people
where the Rembrandts are . . . as shit jobs go, this one's pretty
hard to beat . . . it was a lot like the day I woke up on morphine
in the white room, with all the other jobs and signing on being
the headfucks you had to go through in the rest of the big awful
dysfunctional hospital . . . you were still stuck in the general
hospital but it was a pleasant room with a sunny view out the
window of the world outside . . . I remember one of my first
shifts sitting in a silent room with the light playing gently on
some Monets early in the morning, and one of the old guys who's
been there for years walked past me and sang, 'Its just another
day for you and me in paradise . . .' ironically but also kind of
seriously . . . those vast marble rooms with their Tiepolos and
leather couches felt like the departure lounge for Heaven . . . and
like any departure lounge the key was learning how to wait . . .
even on a bad day, when it seemed like doing time, it was still
doing time in paradise, where your punishment was to look at
the world's greatest artistic achievements for ever . . . the passage

of time becomes acute, it stretches out to infinity like the long columnated marble halls, and with little stimulation from the humdrum and the mundane, you are forced to assess your life deeply from funny angles . . . it was a bit like being Dave at the end of 2001, seeing himself old and then embryonic in that strange white metaphysical mansion, until finally you were just floating somewhere deep in the middle of eternity . . . it also ended up as the perfect discipline I needed to make me focus and write all this down . . . I'd sneak a little notepad in on the sly and just write and write, or at least think about what I was going to write later . . . and I was generally left alone to do so . . . I was normally only ever disturbed by some fifty-year-old yank asking me, 'Gee, doesn't the time drag? Don't you go a little crazy sitting there all day?' and I had to say no . . . no, I couldn't say it drove me crazy, and I didn't mind the time going slow, because in the end it was just another day for me in paradise . . .

8: A Golden Place and Time

I've just bought a pair of loafers, in which I intend to arse about at my ease, engrossed in the noble art of doing sweet FA . . . I'll probably brew a pot of tea . . . sit around and write when the words come . . . I might even venture out for a quiet, poignant evening walk, as long as the sunset is romantic enough . . . the job could have a couple of shifts a week, in its on-off kind of way, and a couple of shifts seemed like a reasonable compromise, as we all need to eat and pay the bills, and occasionally buy some loafers . . .

I was sitting on the couch absentmindedly looking out the window . . . a dog was sniffing along the floor, caught in the long shadows . . . a telephone wire moved noiselessly in the breeze . . . the tops of the buildings turned into gold, as if infused with a mysterious inner glow . . . in the distance the cranes slowly swayed, the gold gave way to rose, and the sunset comes and goes . . . the evening's drenched in dying sunlight, and once again I'm graced by my perfect hour . . .in the silence of that shitty room a secret unfolds, a secret that will always be a secret, a secret I don't understand, and words like these will always fail . . .

The guilty thrill of not answering the repeated knocks on the door, of ignoring your phone for days; missing friends' birthdays, the abandoned friends you haven't seen for months; not supporting people in times of need, depression, trouble . . . the guilty liberation of deliberately letting all social commitments slide, and going missing from your own life, into an empty and enchanting freedom of notebooks, long walks, long thoughts . . .

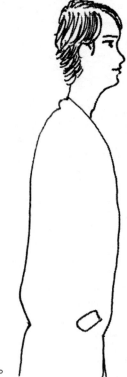

I've been wandering the streets again, losing myself under a balmy lilac sky . . . the lonely romance you undertake with the city, wasting an evening discovering her parks and stations . . . walking for the sake of it, the journey as the destination, a journey conducted at dawdling pace, taking in the scenic spots: the enigma of a filthy alley, the little bit of scrub behind the viaduct that comes to be your own . . . disconnecting oneself from one's allotted place, to drift unknown into the labyrinths and curiosity shop windows of the world . . .

There was a lane in London that brought me closer to life . . . a
road that became my ramshackle paradise . . . I would wander
up and down, staring at its dreamy neon signs at night, and feel
like I'd found my place in the world . . . I'd wander around
slowly and linger on corners, and the hookers would pester me
for business, thinking I was after a good seeing to, when really I
was only interested in the atmosphere and the crumbling buildings
and the way they caught the light . . . I must have looked a bit
sinister or soft in the head, mumbling to myself, scribbling away
in my notepad . . . one night I remember stopping in front of
this shabby old shed near the railway bridge and staring at it for

a long time, like I was in some strange trance, feeling as happy as I'd ever felt, and realizing very clearly that we all live in an invisible paradise . . . on the Sunday market the shed would be opened and a quiff-headed rockabilly guy would play boogie woogie piano in it . . . the market sold anything, absolutely anything, the best example I can remember being a crushed up ping-pong ball with a hole in it on sale for 10p . . . next to that particular stall was a derelict building with half a roof and a hand painted sign saying ART with an arrow pointing up some very old and unsafe stairs . . . and on the scrubby waste ground behind it an old Bengali man in a sarong was taming a beautiful white horse while devotional songs drifted over the scene from the minaret up the road . . . the place seemed to exist in its own reality, a reality that had escaped the gravitational pull of (Starbucks) and normal market forces . . . people did things their own way round here, people like the crusty transvestite beggar you'd see doing the rounds on an evening, or people like Old Tom, who slept in the back of his stinky camper van in his dilapidated yard, who was always covered head to toe in soot and grease, but had achieved a strange kind of freedom . . . for a passing moment, before the luxury flats and the (Starbucks) staked their inevitable claim, that place offered a genuine glimpse of freedom, of possibilities you hadn't thought of before, and that lane, a stone's throw from the grind of the global financial zone, seemed to be gathering together another kind of England, and its shanty backstreets and tenements became the open and welcoming refuge of England's dreaming . . .

I ended up on Wapping High Street one evening, sunkissed and bearded in flip-flops, jotting it all down, surrounded by all these clean-shaven fitness freaks . . . you see scores of them, veins popping out their heads, willing themselves further, planning how they're gonna clench that corporate deal at work in the morning . . . disgusting . . . I saw a Japanese guy in chinos and a sweater over his shoulders pretending to take golf swings, real driving ones, his expression contorted into pure blind competitive ambition . . . I wanted to take a golf club to his evil little fucking face . . . Wapping was beautiful though; I discovered the pub that Turner had bought for his mistress . . . I asked the barman if I could take a look round but he physically barred my way and spoke to me with utter disdain, as if I was a dirty tramp or something, which I suppose is an easy mistake to make . . . compared to all those fucking corporate joggers I suppose I am very much like a tramp, except I have somewhere to sleep at night and I can turn all the shit into gold by writing about it . . . we both stumble through the evening, walking for miles, lingering at the sunny crossroads of the city, dishevelled and out of it, our eyes far away somewhere that seems to scare the evil joggers and arsehole barmen . . . maybe they read something suspicious in the aimless wandering, read some purpose into it . . . I assure you there is no purpose other than the fact it makes my mind function as I would like it to, clean and pure so the good thoughts come and I can slowly fill up empty notepads . . . if we are losers its because we love to lose ourselves under a balmy sunset, and watch the evening become transfigured into something magical, as if the sunset were some kind of alchemical crucible, and for an hour or so the dirty streets are paved with gold, and we forget ourselves and fade into the sun . . .

I was walking down a leafy avenue in town when this tramp started hassling me for some change . . . as I was telling him that I was skint he broke out in a big smile like he recognized me and asked where I was from . . . it turned out he was from the Old Country too . . . I couldn't place him but when he told me I remembered who he was: Eddie Lee, the legendary wino who used to beg outside the multi-storey carpark next to Kwik Save . . . we talked for a bit . . .it made me feel good to see someone from up there . . . I asked him what he was doing down here and he pointed at his mates and explained how they'd all come down to London for a bit of an extended holiday . . . it made me laugh to think that even wino tramps from the Old Country get to go on holiday . . . I stayed for a bit, and then as we said our goodbyes he asked me to pass on his best wishes to his younger brother Alfie (the legendary gluey) if I was ever passing through the multi-storey carpark back home . . .

The highlight of the summer was definitely my business trip to Florence . . . a guy whose shop I'd worked in had invited me out there with him to try and sell his new clothes range to the Italians . . . the fashion fair was held in Pitti, an old fascist army barracks just outside the historic city centre that is now used to host shows and fairs and spectaculars . . . we got there dazed and disoriented from a long hot trip, thrown into this strange civilization where everything felt pretty unreal anyway, but nothing prepared me for Pitti . . . Pitti was like a magician's trick . . . the whole scene had the entirely artificial air of Art Deco LA, the era of Valentino and Charlie Chaplin and the legendary big studios of Holywood's lost golden age, an enormous stage set like a city in miniature . . . when we arrived the show was only half up, as the dying sun laid flat colours across palm trees and theatrical props and huge plywood boards, with giraffes and jugglers and dwarves with fake wings wandering across the set, waiting around, eating ice creams . . . it was one of those situations you walk into that make you realize life is just very dreamlike and wonderful after all . . .

My favourite drinking buddy for the trip was my boss's dad who just came along for a laugh . . . I ended up in all these snazzy Italian winebars with a fifty-five-year-old Manc rugby player with cauliflower ears who was constantly pissed up trying to fuck all the teenage Italian totty . . . grabbing their arses and generally disgracing himself . . . he would get arseholed and the lines between fun and trouble were constantly being tested . . . on the last night we were in the corner of a nightclub and he told all these roughneck African drug dealers to fuck off and then ended up befriending them and giving them high fives in that crap way dads do when they're trying to be cool . . . they loved him by the time we left, he was their new best friend . . . and I suppose he was mine as well . . . what a guy, he just didn't give a flying fuck . . . and wherever you are now, captain, I salute you . . .

1st new picture

Some nights I left them to it and got away on my own to wander the winding streets . . . they thought I was a bit bookish and odd, looking round the churches and alleys all night but I thought, fuck 'em, let them drink their Stella in the Irish bar, I was far happier and far more intoxicated by the riddle of this city . . . I would just take off, notepad in pocket, and get lost for a few hours, away from the bars and the Yankees and Germans, well into the local neighbourhoods . . . one night I wandered over the river and up the hill, past Galileo's house, the house where he discovered the Earth obeys simple mechanical laws of motion and goes round the sun like clockwork . . . a little bit further and I was on what was virtually a country road . . . the dusk was creeping in with that warm fecund summer twilight where the crickets hum constantly all around you . . . I realized I was lost among fields of pungent garlic and suddenly these bats swarmed all around me, against the silhouette of the castle on the hill . . . and again a blinker was momentarily lifted from my eyes and I twigged that life resembles a fairytale, and being awake might just be another layer of dreaming . . .

When all the hard work was done we went up into the hills to this flash fashion party in a Renaissance villa . . . Florence isn't like London or Paris with big sprawling suburbs, once you're outside the historical centre to your amazement you're straightaway driving through rolling countryside densely littered with farms and villas like the beginning of a city that hasn't joined up yet . . . we pulled up to the pad on the hill . . . the next thing I knew I was lying in a pool with a glass of champagne and a joint floating about appreciating the sunset . . . there were fat characters walking around in white dressing gowns smoking cigars . . . it was like a cross between Miami Vice and the Club Tropicana video . . . I relaxed into it and floated around and had my golden moment, knowing this might never happen to me again . . . as I bobbed around I watched the heavy sun sinking between the lush Tuscan hills, stoned out of my tiny mind, realizing this was the closest thing to the archetypal vision of paradise I ever saw, and once again I was washed over with that wonderful feeling that life was somehow secretly enchanted and dreamlike and unreal, as I sat in a pool somewhere in the solar system while an enormous red sun set in the far horizon like the centre of some ridiculous and beautiful Galilean clockwork . . .

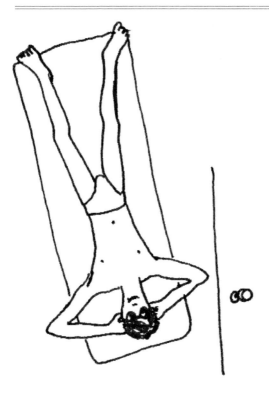

Once upon a time I was alive, and experienced various things, and generally didn't notice . . . but occasionally it hit me, and I was amazed by the beauty and strangeness and pain in the arse of life . . . the mystery of walking down a street, breathing, and that I was even there at all . . . and though I knew it was only my life and nothing much ever really happened in it, and one way or another all these things I saw and loved would be forgotten, I was amazed how mysterious and meaningful it all seemed to me, in my misery and happiness and ignorance and inklings, and I knew I was lucky to have dreamed this dream . . .